SANDSTORMS and SURGERY

(The DeBakey Factor)

By Robert J. Salem, M.D.,
F.A.C.S.

FOREWORD

In "Sandstorms and Surgery (The DeBakey Factor)," Dr. Robert Salem has shared many of the intimate details of the personal and professional relationship between him and my husband, a relationship that spanned more than five decades.

My husband, Dr. Michael DeBakey, was a major influence on Dr. Salem throughout his career, and it is easily discerned within the pages of this book that Dr. DeBakey held a special place in Dr. Salem's heart. Likewise, Dr. DeBakey had a great deal of admiration for Dr. Salem and held him in high esteem, as evidenced by Dr. Salem's selection as President-elect of the DeBakey International Surgical Society beginning in 2010.

Part of their mutual bonding was the common Lebanese heritage they shared. My husband invited Dr. Salem to attend the Congressional Gold Medal Ceremony in Washington, D.C., in April 2008. Dr. Salem was asked to stand guard at his casket in City Hall following his death in July 2008. I believe Dr. Salem's book will help preserve the incredible medical legacy of my husband, a legacy that has touched countless lives and spans around the world. It is my pleasure to contribute to this book on behalf of Dr. DeBakey. I know he would have been proud.

Mrs. Katrin DeBakey

Dr. Bob Salem and his career are perfect examples of the "Spirit of West Texas" which is; "One can accomplish almost anything if they persistently work hard."

His academic achievements, starting in the small town of Sudan, Texas persisted through Texas Tech, UT Southwestern Medical School and Baylor Surgical Residency culminated not only in his surgical leadership roles in West Texas, but the whole state of Texas.

His descriptions of all the phases of his educational and professional life are not only fascinating, but inspirational to all of us, especially me.

O. Wayne Isom, M.D.
Professor and Chairman, Department of Cardiothoracic Surgery,
Terry Allen Kramer Professor of Cardiothoracic Surgery, Weill Cornell Medical College,
New York-Presbyterian Hospital/Weill Cornell Medical Center, New York, New York

Idalou and Lubbock, Texas! We thought all cardiac surgeons came from New York or Los Angeles! Well, if it were not for these great cities, Larry King would have ended his career in 1987 when he had quintuple by-pass surgery.

How did these cities save the legendary broadcaster? Well they did so by bringing in one of the world's great surgeons, Dr. Wayne Isom, who saved Larry's life on December 1, 1987.

In many speeches given today, my father likes to recount the time he first met the Texan who was going to save his life. The story is absolutely hysterical and if you can see Larry tell it, do yourself a favor and see it!

From their humble beginnings, Dr. Isom and Dr. Robert Salem learned from the best! Their friendship and connection to their hometown has never left them. Dr. Salem took it one step further by having the vision in honoring Dr. Isom in Lubbock that lives every day. As you are reading this book the miracles continue at the Covenant Children's Hospital Isom Heart Center for Children.

The name Isom is connected to King for the rest of their lives and will be their legacy too. The Larry King Cardiac Foundation has selected only three children's hospitals in the United States, and we are proud to have this Covenant/Isom Heart part of the team. The work done there each day is a testament to its employees; they are some of the most dedicated people you will ever run into!

So when someone mentions Texas, we do not think of Dallas or Houston. We think of Lubbock, where miracles in lifesaving care are helping us Save a Heart a Day!

We are proud to see the names of Salem, Isom and King carried forward in the years to come in providing this help to others.

Regards,
Larry King, *Founder Larry King Cardiac Foundation*
Larry King, Jr. *President*

TABLE OF CONTENTS

Chapter 6 – Houston, Texas – Baylor College of Medicine Residency

Chapter 7 – Lubbock, Texas – Return To

ACKNOWLEDGMENTS

First and foremost I owe a huge debt of gratitude to my assistant, Denise Brunner. She has assisted and collaborated with me on every aspect of this book and I am deeply appreciative and grateful to her for all of her steadfast and loyal hard work, as well as sharing with me a passion for recording history.

Doug Hensley has spent more than 25 years as a writer and journalist with the Avalanche Journal in Lubbock, Texas. His past interests have been primarily in the sports world, but more recently have expanded to include Lubbock's medical heritage and he has written many articles about the evolution of medicine in Lubbock. He and I have collaborated on many aspects of the medical history in Lubbock contained in this book and he also has been a valuable resource for me on many other aspects of the book, as he has been for other authors as well. Doug is a Texas Tech graduate with a degree in Journalism and has served as an adjunct professor in the Texas Tech College of Mass Communications.

Linda Guillory is an experienced transcriptionist at Covenant Health System and was trained several years ago by Mary Wisnewski, who was a transcriptionist for Dr. Michael DeBakey in Houston. Linda took my original handwritten notes and transcribed them into a readable coherent text and I am deeply indebted to her.

Dr. Gerry Maddoux is a long time friend and colleague. He is a highly regarded interventional cardiologist and in recent years has evolved into an accomplished author and radio talk show participant. His valuable and insightful suggestions for my book have been deeply appreciated.

Ron Roberts, the Chief Meteorologist at KMAC TV in Lubbock, Texas, is a popular speaker and a strong patient advocate for preventative cardiovascular diseases. He and his wife, Wendy, have collaborated on a book - "Return" - about Ron's recent acute illness and have offered many suggestions on my book, which have been invaluable.

Kathy Drake, a long time friend, and owner of Drake Photography in Lubbock, Texas, has photographed many of the pictures in this book, and her superb works have enhanced so very much this body of work. Her photographic genius through the years has captured many spectacular events at Covenant Health System.

I would be negligent not to mention all of the many people associated with Covenant Health System – the Board, the Administrative Staff, the Medical Staff, the Nursing Staff, the other support staff – all of whom have contributed so much in providing me with the platform and support with which to practice my art for so many years. I thank you all.

And finally to my lovely wife, Kay, who has steadfastly stood by me through peaks and valleys, happy days and sad days, rigorous schedules, nights without sleep – but constantly happy, smiling and vivacious and encouraging me to record my life's work. Thank you, dear Kay.

I expect to pass through this world but once; any good thing therefore that I can do, or any kindness that I can show to any fellow creature, let me do it now; let me not defer or neglect it, for I shall not pass this way again.

Ettiene De Grellet
(1773-1855)

1
SUDAN, TEXAS

Sandstorms and Tumbleweeds

As I look back on the early days of my childhood in the small country farming town of Sudan in West Texas in the 30s and 40s, my most vivid memory is the incessant, blinding sandstorms accompanied by hordes of rolling tumbleweeds, some three to four feet in diameter, catapulted across the flat lands and roads by those tornadic-like winds. I remember so clearly the wind howling outside our house on the West Texas prairie that it sometimes kept me awake, and by morning the windstorm had pushed small grains of sand through an unseen space to settle on my windowsill. I can remember also walking that half-mile to school many days with a handkerchief over my face and nose to diminish the amount of sand I might inhale, and clearly can still see the tumbleweeds piled up several feet high on the sides of the houses as I trekked to school. One of my graduation presents from high school in 1946, not given as a joke but as a practical gift, was a facemask, which I frequently used to wear over my entire face.

On several occasions, while driving my parents' car from Sudan to Lubbock, a distance of some 50 miles, I got caught in such fierce sandstorms with winds greater than 50 miles per hour that I could only drive 5 to 10 miles per hour because it was so black, I couldn't tell if I was on the highway or driving off into the ditch on the side of the road. In the middle of the day the sun was obscured by this thick, brown dirt and sand, so thick that you needed your car lights on, but so dense that they were of no benefit.

I thought at the time that West Texas must have been the sandstorm and tumbleweed capital of the world, although I have read where others lay claim to that dubious title.

This was the setting in those days when all of the farming was "dry land" with the farmers depending entirely on rainfall to water their crops, and before they were aware that there was water underground that could be brought up through water wells to provide the much-needed moisture for their crops to thrive. Subsequently over the next decade, water wells were drilled to irrigate the crops, moisten the land

and settle some of the sand. In addition to the water wells, the farmers acquired more knowledge about crop rotations and with the natural climatic condition changes, the weather conditions gradually and slowly improved.

Sudan was incorporated in 1925, and my parents moved there six years later, during the Great Depression, to establish a dry goods store when I was 2 years of age. The population in 1930 was 1,024 and the high-water mark was 1,336 in 1950. Since then there has been a steady decline, like many rural West Texas towns, to a low of 999 in 2009.

Family

After we moved to Sudan, my only sibling, a sister, Betty, was born. For a period of time we didn't even have a house to live in, but lived in the back of our parents' store. Later on we obtained a small home, for which dad paid $25.00 and two pair of overalls, that my parents lived in until the time of their deaths.

Betty and I were fortunate to have kind, loving and generous parents. What I remember most about my parents, both of whom lived long lives, was about their lives of giving and sacrifice. They never were wealthy and never had any aspirations to be so. Rather, they, and particularly my father, felt that material things in life were of secondary importance to a life of giving and helping others. They had a successful small country town dry good store in which they labored to earn a decent living for themselves, my sister and me, but we never had anything extravagant.

We read the Bible every night as a family unit and never had a meal of any kind without saying a grace or blessing beforehand, and we took turns doing this.

My dad sold his store at a relatively young age because he wanted to devote himself to a full-time lay Christian ministry to help the underprivileged children in our area. He converted his store into a haven for children on Saturday mornings. Part of the store was changed into an area of various games – pool, ping-pong, etc. The other part was configured for a place of worship. Through a nonprofit organization called LOTWS (Love Overcometh The Worlds) he would assemble all

2

of the children, usually some 30 or 40, every Saturday morning for a couple of hours of working. He had arranged for the children to have odd jobs with other business people or farmers in the area, and they would work for a period of time and he would pay them for their work out of monies donated to the organization, trying to teach them to work for what they got rather than to accept or ask for a handout. After the work session, they would all reconvene back at the store for an hour or two of recreational activity and then end the morning with a devotional program that he or invited pastors or other people would provide. This typifies his life. After our mother died, Dad continued with a life of love, giving, and personal sacrifice. He lived comfortably and warmly in the little house we grew up in and had the necessities of life, but not many other amenities. I would bring him food, clothes, and extra money, but he would always give it away to others he felt were more needy than he. I was never at his home that four or five people would come by knocking on his door asking for something – anything, and he would always give them something – $2, $3, $5, food, a pair of old shoes, an old sweater or something.

He patterned his life after that of Christ and interpreted the Bible literally, and perhaps too literally some would say. I'm sure some people thought he was a religious fanatic, but I have never known a more Christ-like person who lived and taught the basic tenets of Christian living and life than he.

Moral Compass

He was the moral compass in my life and was given the Evangelistic Award from the Northwest Texas Conference of the Methodist Church one year for his evangelistic efforts with the children of Sudan and neighboring areas.

He was my biggest referral source by far when I later started my surgical practice in Lubbock. I had a countless number of patients come to me for surgery whom I didn't even know because of the reputation of my father. They always said that if I were Joe Salem's son, I had to be okay because he was such a great figure of faith and integrity to them. What a tremendous legacy he and my mom left me and my sister – no monetary inheritance, but a boundless and endless cache of Christian faith and love.

Our Mom, who was raised in Spur, Texas, as a child, was always there for Betty and me. She always supported my dad and his Christian, evangelistic work, but probably sacrificed personally more than he, of necessity. She was a religious person in her own right, but she didn't have the zealous enthusiasm my dad did. She had a series of heart attacks in the latter years of her life, and I always remember what she said to me as we drove up to her little house following one of her hospitalizations – "Be it ever so humble, there's no place like home."

Childhood Memories

Childhood memories in Sudan were all pleasant, centered around family, sports and church activities. We didn't have much in the way of material things, but what we had was adequate. I didn't know any different and was always happy. I enjoyed being a Boy Scout and attained the rank of an Eagle Scout and always looked forward every summer to the Boy Scout camps in Post, Texas. I worked in my dad's department store part-time and in the summers worked at various jobs. One summer I worked as a laborer mixing concrete by hand in a wheelbarrow and helped build one of the grain elevators still present in the town. On other occasions I worked on the farms doing odd jobs. During the summer months I hoed weeds in the cotton fields, and in the fall I put a cotton sack over my shoulder and pulled bolls one at a time as was done in those days before the large mechanical cotton picking machines were developed.

The "Rainmaker"

One summer I worked on a farm owned by the Raymond Nix family. Their son-in-law, Jay Miller, was a U.S. Air Force veteran and had married Raymond's daughter, Berneice. He and I were out irrigating the cotton one summer, and irrigation in those days was done row by row with a plastic siphon tube. There was a large ditch at one end of the cotton fields that carried the water, and the rows of the cotton ran perpendicular to this large water supply ditch. We would go row by row of cotton and fill up the siphon tubes with water to provide water to each row of cotton individually. This was a backbreaking job and the tubes were constantly malfunctioning, and we would have to back up and get them started again by immersing one end of the tube, which was a one-half circle, in the water ditch again, filling it with water and then rapidly bringing the other end out and placing it in the cotton row. Learning this siphon technique would bode well for me later in my life, as you will hear about in a subsequent chapter. So, one day Jay was looking up longingly at the clouds and I'm sure reminiscing about his flying days in the US Air Force, and said to me, "Bob, there must be a better and easier way to irrigate this cotton than what we're doing. Why don't we see if we can't make it rain?" Well, I had no idea what he was talking about, but I was all for trying something different. He said he had heard about people making it rain by seeding the clouds with dry ice and other things. So, he said, "Let's go try that" and I said, "Man, let's go. I'm for anything besides what we're doing."

So, we went into town and he rented a two-seater airplane. We went to the local drug store and bought several bags of dry ice. He took the bags of dry ice and went up in the airplane alone, and I could see him flying through the clouds overhead for a while, but no rain came. I lost him for a while and continued on with my siphon tube irrigation, when I was startled by the sound of an airplane at my back. I abruptly turned around and there was Jay coming directly toward me, only 30-40 yards away, flying so low the wheels of the plane were hitting the tops of the cotton stalks. I immediately hit the ground with a "belly buster" landing in a pool of mud and water.

Jay came back a while later and jokingly said, "Did I scare you?" and I said, "Well, what do you think?" He said, "Bob, this is a two-man operation, so come on and let's make another run and you sit in the rear seat and man the ice." So, we went flying through the clouds again over the Nix farm with me sitting in the rear seat feverishly dumping out the dry ice into the clouds as we flew through them. Well, regardless of other people's results, our efforts were futile, and the next day we were laboring in the hot sun again with our siphon tubes.

Lunches at the Nix farm were something you could only dream about – chicken-fried steak, fried chicken, mashed potatoes and gravy, homemade rolls, fresh corn on the cob, green beans and black-eyed peas grown on the farm, homemade butter and buttermilk, and cobblers of all kinds – peach, cherry, apple. I would have worked all day for no pay just to have lunch each day with this wonderful family and their incredible meals.

Today Dr. Tim Nix, grandson of Raymond Nix and nephew of Jay and Berneice Miller, is a PhD at Texas Tech University Health Sciences Center. He is Director of the MBA and MD/MBA program and the Health Maintenance Organization, and I have the opportunity to visit with him on frequent occasions.

Later in my career I would have the occasion to operate on Berneice for a breast cancer.

Another farming experience I have had through the years that continues to this day has to do with the Messamore family of Sudan. Many years ago my dad purchased some acreage near the Nix farm and leased it out to Alvin and Gail Messamore to farm and through a handshake agreement, Dad would take a percentage of the net profits. This arrangement went on for many years until Alvin was suddenly, tragically killed in a motor vehicle accident at a relatively young age on one of the farm roads near the farm.

His son, Haldon, subsequently took over his dad's farming operations with his wife, Kim. I later acquired Dad's farm and through another handshake agreement, Haldon and Kim continue to farm the Salem place today.

Farming is a tough business, dependant so much on climatic and environmental factors – rainfall, hail, insects. It is also a very gratifying experience – to plant a seed in the ground in the spring and watch it grow over the weeks and months into a beautiful, mature plant in the fall, rendering much sought after commodities – cotton, grain, peanuts and wheat.

Having grown up in a farming community, I have always appreciated the many farming families, like the Robert Mastens who had farming land near ours and who were some of my closest friends, some of whom now live in Lubbock (Marty Edwards and Marianne Overton, daughter and granddaughter respectively of Robert Masten). Watching them toil many long hours in the hot sun day in and day out has made me so very respectful of the many people who make farming their life's work.

Arrival in
Sudan (1931)

Salem Store
(1933)

Sudan Square
(1933)

Grain
Elevator

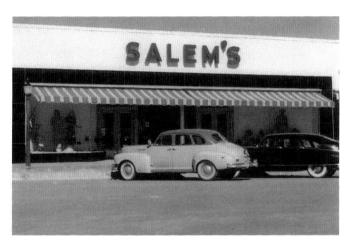

Salem New
Store
(1950)

Beth & Joe
Salem —
LOTWS Park
(1965)

Beth & Joe
Salem
(1985)

Betty Salem
Korioth
(2005)

Betty & Bob
Salem
(1935)

Betty & Bob
Salem —
College Days
(1952)

10

Bob & Betty
with Parents
(1960)

Bob & Betty with
Parents & Grandmother
Harkey
(1962)

Salem
Farm

11

Messamore
Family
(2007)

Salem
Family
Home

Methodist
Church

Sudan
High
School

Betty & Mom
Salem —
Christmas
(1975)

2
LUBBOCK, TEXAS
TEXAS TECH UNIVERSITY

After graduation from Sudan High School, I went on to college at Texas Tech University in Lubbock, Texas. World War II had just ended in 1946 when I started, and Lubbock and the university were  flooded by veterans who had just gotten out of the various services. Consequently, there was no dormitory room or apartment to be found anywhere in Lubbock to rent, so I had to commute back and forth from Sudan to Lubbock every day. I didn't have a car, so transportation to and from Lubbock was a huge problem.

Veteran With a Car

My salvation turned out to be Horace Jay "Doc" Blanchard from Sudan – a veteran with a car. "Doc" was a veteran of WW II and appropriately nicknamed "Doc" after "Doc" Blanchard, the US Army fullback All-American of the famous Mr. "Outside," Glenn Davis and Mr. "Inside," "Doc" Blanchard duo of the No.1 team in the country in 1946 – Army. He gave me a ride back and forth from Sudan every day, and that went on for the entire first semester, after which I finally rented a room from an elderly lady on 8th Street near the campus. There were times when my class schedule didn't mesh with his and I was on my own to get home back to Sudan. So, I would ride a bus, hitchhike (common practice in those days), or on a few occasions walk the last seven miles from Amherst to Sudan.

"Doc" would later become a state senator and be a major political player in the development of the medical school for Texas Tech University, and I also would have the opportunity to operate on him as a patient. He was flying one day when he sustained a blood clot from varicose veins in his leg that traveled to his lung, and he had to undergo emergency surgery from which he recovered without complications. It is incredible that stories and events like this unfold later in one's life.

Texas Tech Basketball

I played basketball on the Tech freshman team, but after the first few months, I realized that I had to devote all my time to my Pre-Med studies and gave up basketball. Freshman hazing was pretty common in those days, and particularly in the athletic dormitory and in the social fraternities. So later in my freshman year when I had a room in Lubbock, I was summoned over to the athletic dorm late at night frequently, where the scholarship players lived, to get my dose of hazing. I remember in particular, Artis Barton, from Springlake, Texas, near Sudan, who was a year ahead of me in high school and now a sophomore at Tech. As a freshman and former competitor in high school, he singled me out in particular for the hazing, but good-spiritedly, and he and I would later become good friends, but I was glad when the hazing was over and I could sit down comfortably without a pillow. Artis was an outstanding ball player for Texas Tech and went on to have a stellar collegiate career.

Silver Keys

Later on I was active in the Texas Tech political activities and served on the student council; I also enjoyed my fraternal relationship with members of the Silver Key fraternity and was later to be president of that fraternity which later became the Phi Delta Theta Greek fraternity. My "Big Brother" in the fraternity turned out to be the brother of Joyce Nix, wife of Bill Nix , Berneice's brother. (Couldn't seem to get away from all of those Nixes!)

Professional Compass

In 1948, Dr. Michael E. DeBakey, generally regarded by many as the "Father of Modern Cardiovascular Surgery" accepted an offer to become Chairman of the Department of Surgery at Baylor College of Medicine in Houston, Texas. As a Pre-Med student at Texas Tech, little did I know or suspect at the time, that only nine years later I would be receiving a telegram and letter from him while I was stationed in Paris, France, in the USAF Medical Corp, that would impact my professional life and career forever, and that he would become my "professional compass" for the remainder of my surgical career. The "DeBakey Factor" in my life was unsuspectingly beginning to unfold.

Doc Blanchard
1924–2009

After his freshman year at North Carolina, in 1942, Felix Anthony Blanchard tried to enlist in the Navy's V-12 program, which allowed students to complete their education in exchange for a service commitment. He was turned down for, among other things, being overweight. The decision came back to haunt the Navy: Doc Blanchard, who died from pneumonia at his home in the Texas town of Bulverde on Sunday, ended up enrolling at West Point, where he led Army's football team to three wins in as many years over the Naval Academy. Following the first, in 1944, Gen. Douglas MacArthur took time out from his duties in the Pacific theater to send a wire: "The greatest of all Army teams.... We have stopped the war to celebrate your magnificent success."

INSIDE MAN
The bullish Blanchard rushed for 1,908 yards and 38 TDs in three seasons.

Blanchard teamed with Glenn Davis to form the most feared and famed backfield of their day. (They appeared on covers of TIME and LIFE.) A battering ram of a fullback, Blanchard was known as Mr. Inside to the athletic Davis's Mr. Outside. (Arthur Daley of *The New York Times* called Blanchard "that berserk water buffalo.") Blanchard became the first junior to win the Heisman in 1945, then Davis won it the next year. In their three years together they led the Cadets to 27 wins and a tie (0–0 against Notre Dame in 1946) in 28 games. Naturally, pro teams were intrigued at the prospect of keeping them together; the San Francisco 49ers of the All-America Football Conference acquired the rights to both players and offered $130,00 apiece over three years, but the Army, fearing a p.r. backlash, refused to alter the terms of their commitments to allow them to play. The only serious football Blanchard ever played after he graduated was at Randolph Field, an Air Force Base in Texas, where he got his wings in 1948. But his postgridiron career was fruitful: Before retiring from the Air Force in 1971, he flew 113 combat missions during the Vietnam War and was awarded a Distinguished Flying Cross.

H. J. "DOC" BLANCHARD
STATE SENATOR

May 3, 1974

28th Senatorial
District Counties:

Andrews
Borden
Cochran
Crosby
Dawson
Ector
Gaines
Garza
Lynn
Lubbock
Martin
Terry
Yoakum

1607 Broadway
Lubbock, Texas
79401

Mr. J. T. Salem
Box 218
Sudan, Texas

Dear Mr. Salem:

I wish to take this means to express my sincere appreciation for your help to further my campaign. Your gesture of support encourages me to continue to stand up for what is right and best for West Texas. Please be assured that, if re-elected, I will do my best to be worthy of your trust.

Thank you for your contribution, but most of all, thanks for your friendship.

Very truly yours,

H. J. "Doc" BLANCHARD

HJB:mj

With much love to each of you - Your prayers are much appreciated

Horace

Pol. Adv. Pd. for by H. J. Blanchard

18

Cast Your Vote
for
BOBBY SALEM

For Arts & Science
Student Council
Representative

TEXAS TECHNOLOGICAL COLLEGE

Lubbock, Texas

April 26, 1950

Dear Bobby:

The Student Council wishes to congratulate you upon the contribution you have made to student leadership on Texas Tech campus during the past year, and as a part of Parents Day, Sunday, May 7, you are invited to take part in the leadership appreciation service, to be held in the Recreation Hall at 1:30.

At your very earliest convenience, will you drop by the Office of the Dean of Men, Administration Building 209, and fill out a blank for us. This will facilitate our planning for this part of Parents Day.

Through the leadership appreciation service the Student Council hopes to express its appreciation for the fine leadership which you and other members of the student body have given so well during the past year. We hope that it will be possible for you to be present on this occasion.

Yours very truly,

Gale Rogers

Gale Rogers, Chairman
Parents Day Committee
Student Council

Marshall Gettys

Marshall Gettys, President
Student Council

3
DALLAS, TEXAS
SOUTHWESTERN MEDICAL SCHOOL

After graduation from Texas Tech with a degree in chemistry and a minor in biology, I moved on to medical school at Southwestern Medical School in Dallas. My parents provided me with my first car at age 21, for which I was equally proud and grateful. Medical school is a blur – constant studying – little social life – and less money. Upon the first day of medical school I felt pressure to succeed academically. Because of the large number of veterans who had returned from World War II who had gained entrance into the medical school at the same time I was, I was delayed a year into being accepted. Once in, I felt somewhat intimidated by the large number of older students, many of whom were from large metropolitan cities.

Gross Anatomy

However, my fears were alleviated somewhat on the day of our first gross anatomy exam. In this exam, all of the cadaver bodies were lined up in the Gross Anatomy Lab, some 30 or 40 of them, and specific anatomic parts on each cadaver were tagged. We had less than one minute to identify the part and write down on a piece of paper what we thought was the correct answer.

On this particular day I was standing outside the Anatomy Lab by Tom Regnier (we were always seated alphabetically so Regnier and Salem were always side by side). Tom had been an Air Force pilot during World War II and he said to me, "Bob, you know, I've flown 30 bombing runs over Germany, been shot at with anti-aircraft guns, wounded and received the Purple Heart, and I've been frightened beyond belief many times, but you know what – I've never been as scared as I am right now." I thought to myself, with some comfort and relief from my apprehension, that even guys like Tom Regnier are feeling the pressure, too, and it's not just only from this little insignificant guy from Sudan, Texas.

I thoroughly enjoyed learning about the human body (physiology, anatomy, biochemistry, etc.) and all of the disease entities and treatments in all of the clinical disciplines like Surgery, OB/Gyn, Pediatrics, etc., but the accumulation of knowledge did not come easy for me and I studied diligently several hours daily. Gradually, I developed an organized systematic approach to studying and ended up graduating in the upper 10 percent of my class, some validation of my rather shaky and insecure start. I had some spare time during the summer months after medical school classes were over, and I needed to find some type of work, but I really had no particular skill sets. The only thing I knew anything about was working in the cotton fields hoeing, pulling and irrigating cotton, and a little bit about the retail business, having worked some in my dad's department store in Sudan.

Levine's Department Store

So, I thought the better of the two choices was to look for a job at a department store. Levine's Department Store hired me at minimum wage as a general flunky and sales person. I didn't mind the general flunky part, but hated the salesman part. I overheard the manager of the store one day talking to another employee and he said, "You know, that Salem boy is really a nice young man, but he really isn't much of a salesman." Well, that obviously deflated my ego a bit, but I held on for the rest of the summer, and looked for something different by the next summer.

Baylor Hospital

I secured a job the following years as a nurse's aide at Baylor Hospital. Even though my chores and responsibility initially were menial, I really felt much more comfortable in a hospital environment caring for sick patients than trying to sell a pair of shoes to some little old lady. The head nurse one day asked me to give some injections, and I hadn't ever received any training by anyone to do that, so I confessed to her that I had no experience with that nor with starting IVs, which she also wanted me to do. So, she very quickly got an orange and shoved the needle end of the syringe into the orange and said, "You see, it's really pretty simple – now you try it." So, after two or three orange injections I felt comfortable working on live patients. As my skills and experience rapidly improved, I very soon was given more responsibilities and as my medical knowledge increased year by year in medical school also, I evolved from a nurse's aide to a "quasi" doctor very rapidly. I worked each year on the same floor and by my senior year the nurses were coming to me for advice as to what to do for a sick patient. So I found that experience extremely helpful, not only in the area of patient care, but it gave me a much deeper appreciation for nurses and the responsibility they have in caring for patients.

My first daughter, Cynthia, was born during my third year of medical school. Earning that MD degree was a tremendous achievement for a young lad from Sudan, Texas, and I was eager to practice my trade, but the Air Force called and I substituted my scrub suit temporarily for the Air Force blue uniform.

THIRTEENTH

Commencement Exercises

THE UNIVERSITY OF TEXAS

SOUTHWESTERN MEDICAL SCHOOL

MONDAY, JUNE SIXTH

NINETEEN HUNDRED FIFTY-FIVE

EIGHT O'CLOCK P.M.

MCFARLIN MEMORIAL AUDITORIUM : DALLAS, TEXAS

4

DENVER, COLORADO
FITZSIMMONS ARMY HOSPITAL

During my medical school years, the Korean War was going on and there were compulsory military draft obligations for all young men 18 and older and fit for duty. I fit into that category and was drafted, but given a deferment to finish medical school, with an obligation to enter into the service as soon as I completed my MD degree.

So, immediately upon graduation I was commissioned as a 1st Lieutenant in the USAF Medical Corp and assigned to Fitzsimmons Army Hospital in Denver, Colorado, to start a rotating internship. Overall I enjoyed my surgical rotation the best, which ultimately led to my pursuing a surgical residency and a surgical career.

First Appendectomy
I did my first appendectomy at Fitzsimmons assisted by a Lieutenant Colonel surgeon, and the exhilaration I experienced only intensified my desire to become a real surgeon. I had seen the patient, made the diagnosis and then informed my superior that I thought the patient needed surgery. After he confirmed the diagnosis, he instructed me to schedule the patient with the O.R. with me as the surgeon. I felt an immense sense of exhilaration and self-confidence – I was a real doctor and going to perform a major surgical procedure.

The surgery went quite well, but I'm sure the Colonel could have done it in half the time, but nevertheless he complimented me and I thought to myself, "Man, I have arrived! I am a real dude surgeon!"

President Dwight D. "Ike" Eisenhower
One major event while I was at Fitzsimmons changed the course of my life. The President of the United States at the time was Dwight David Eisenhower, and he was married to Mamie Doud, whose parents lived in Denver. President and Mrs. Eisenhower were in Denver in September 1956. He had played golf at the Fitzsimmons Army Hospital golf course and had sustained his first heart attack. He was seen in the

emergency room and ultimately admitted to the hospital. He had been a heavy, four-pack-a-day cigarette smoker, and it was reported that the day before, his meals had consisted of sausage, ham and pancakes for breakfast, cheeseburger and French fries for lunch, and lamb chops at dinner – not exactly a "heart-healthy diet."

Upon his admission, the top two floors of the hospital were evacuated and all entrances, exits, elevators and stairways were secured by Secret Service personnel. Those of us who might have contact with the President were given added security clearance. His initial evaluation revealed an acute myocardial infarction and treatment was started. Then Dr. Paul Dudley White, the nation's foremost cardiologist from Boston, was consulted. He came to Fitzsimmons and concurred that he had indeed sustained a significant myocardial infarction. Treatment for heart attacks in the 1950s was limited – bed rest, oxygen and blood thinners. He had been advised previously to reduce his smoking habits to one pack per day from his four pack-a-day habit. Today, of course, most people know that cigarette smoking is an absolute "no-no", identified as a major risk factor for coronary and peripheral vascular disease, as well as for lung cancer. But at least 50 years ago it was recognized as a contributory cause and it was recommended that he decrease, at least, his voracious cigarette habit.

He was hospitalized for several weeks, but the affairs of the country were successfully run from the top two floors of Fitzsimmons Army Hospital, and he was finally discharged following an uneventful course. I had occasion to meet him during his hospitalization, but did not of course, as a 1st Lieutenant Intern, have any direct responsibility for his medical care. That was the responsibility of the "Bird" Colonels and higher. He, to this day, has been one of my favorite Presidents and I have no doubt been influenced by this and subsequent events. But this would not be the last time I would have the opportunity to interact with "Ike" and we'll learn more about that in Chapter 5 – Paris, France.

Before being elected the 34th President of the United States, President Eisenhower had been a five-Star General in the United States Army. He served as Supreme Commander of all Allied Forces in Europe during World War II and was the principal figure for planning the successful invasion of France on "D-Day," June 6, 1944, the day his second son, John, graduated from West Point. He, himself, was a West

Point graduate, where he had a great interest in sports.

After his military career and many wartime successes, he became a national hero. After his return from Europe, a movement started to elect him President and he won a landslide victory in 1952, and in 1956 he was re-elected for a second term. He left a long and storied legacy of service to his country and is considered by many as one of our country's most popular Presidents.

Assignment to France

Toward the end of our internships, we each were asked to give a preference of where we might like to spend the next two years of our obligatory military service, and usually those requests were granted. I requested to be assigned to a base anywhere in Texas. I thought that in all probability I would end up practicing somewhere in Texas and this would give me some familiarity with practice opportunities in Texas.

To my surprise and chagrin, I was assigned to a USAF hospital at Orly Airfield in Paris, France. When I mentioned this to an intern friend, who knew I had requested Texas, he said, "Paris, how far is that from Dallas?" I said, "Well, it's Paris, France, not Paris, Texas, and it's about 5,000 miles." He was a bachelor who had wanted and requested to go anywhere in the world. He told them that he didn't want to stay in the states, as he was single and free, and would like to see some of the world. He told them to just send him anywhere in the world – he didn't care. He was totally devastated when the assignments were posted and he got sent to, of all places, Victoria, Texas. We all had great difficulty in trying to figure out why, as a single person, he could easily go anywhere and here I was, married now with two children and had requested to go to Texas but was assigned to a highly sought after strategic hospital in Paris, France. It didn't make a lot of sense, but that's the way it was.

Travel to McGuire Air Force Base, New Jersey

Traveling to McGuire Air Force Base, New Jersey, the point of our departure, in the middle of the summer in a 1956 two-toned, yellow and white Chevrolet - with no air conditioner - with my second daughter, Shelley, a four-week-old baby who was born near the end of my

27

internship, and a two-year-old, was quite an unforgettable experience.

We traveled all night because it was cooler and tried to sleep some during the day at motels. If that wasn't bad enough, our baby had diarrhea and I had tried everything I knew to stop it, and finally just stopped her formula and gave her whole milk, which miraculously worked.

When we finally arrived at McGuire Air Force Base, there was a problem with my passport and visa, and we were detained for 10 days staying in a one room Air Force barracks. I finally called our Congressman, George Mahon, an old friend of my father, who helped get our problem resolved, and he sent my passport and visa by special courier from Washington, and then we were on our way to Paris with 120 other servicemen, wives and crying children. At this point we were totally exhausted and as we boarded the airplane there was this indescribable anxiousness and yet simultaneous exhilaration about the exciting new adventure we were embarking upon. We made the flight to Paris okay and landed at Orly Airfield, Paris, France, on my oldest daughter's second birthday, August 29, 1956.

General of the Army
Dwight D. Eisenhower

AFCSG-24.1   24 May 1955

        Robert J. Salem, M.D.
    ■ 3100 Cornell
      Dallas, Texas.

Dear Doctor

        In the next few weeks you will receive military service orders
placing you on active duty effective on/about 24 Jun.55 The effective
date of active duty is the date you are authorized to begin travel and
you should not begin travel before that date.

        You are being assigned to 1079th Medical Service Squadron, Ftizsimons,
Army Hospital, Denver, Colorado, for duty as intern

The authorized travel time between your present address and your new
station will be indicated in your letter orders.

        The date and assignment indicated above is definite notwithstanding
any previous information you may have received from this office.

        If you have not received Department of the Air Force Orders
within twenty (20) days of your scheduled reporting date, request
you contact the Chief, Medical Utilization Branch, Office of the
Surgeon General, Washington 25, D. C., telephone: EMerson 2-9600,
Extension 82.

                        Sincerely,

                        WILLIE C. MAGNESS
                        Lt. Colonel, USAF (MSC)
                        Chief, Medical Staff Control Division
                        Office of the Surgeon General

29

Intern Class Fitzsimmons Army Hospital — 1956

5
PARIS, FRANCE
USAF HOSPITAL ORLY AIRFIELD

French House

The next two years of my life were the two most eventful in my entire life. We made a decision to live in an old two-story French house not too far from the air base rather than stay in government housing on base. It was heated by a coal furnace in the basement and I fought that thing for the next two years trying to learn how to stoke it at night and keep it smoldering through the night without burning out, and at the same time not start a raging fire at 2 o'clock in the morning. We had a garden, a garage, and a large fenced-in lot for our two girls to play. Our landlady and all of our neighbors were French, and no one spoke a word of English, so that was a challenge at first until we picked up a little conversational French.

Everybody at the air base wanted to know where I was from, and I was always proud to say I was originally from Sudan, Texas. They would say where in the world is Sudan and I would say, "You mean to tell me you've never heard of the tri-city area of the South Plains – Sudan, Muleshoe and Circleback, the Sandstorm and Tumbleweed Capital of the World?" After that, when I would came into the hospital they would say, "Here comes that sandstorm, tumbleweed doctor from Texas."

Normandy Beaches

We employed a French housekeeper whose home was in Normandy, and she spoke not a word of English, but we managed to communicate initially with sign language. Then later on she picked up a little English and I had picked up a little French, and we did a lot better. She had no means of travel except by train or bus, and every month or two I would drive her from Paris to see her family in Normandy. I had the opportunity to walk up and down the beaches of Normandy where only 12 years earlier the Allied Forces began the invasion and liberation of Europe from Nazi occupation. Normandy is located on the northern coast of France along the English Channel and is quite beautiful. I was overwhelmed at the sight of dozens upon dozens of old German bunkers that were still in place all along the coast line. These bunkers were reinforced concrete pillars for housing machine guns and antitank guns, and they were lined up all along the beachheads. I could only imagine what it was like on those beaches only a few years earlier on June 6, 1944, which is commonly referred to as "D-Day," that many historians think is the single most important day in the history of our nation.

Lt Hub Hyatt, Battle of the Bulge
U.S. Military Cemetery, Belgium

After the invasion, with thousands of casualties, the Allied Forces forged east across France and Belgium, and ultimately on into Germany. My uncle, Lt. Hub Hyatt, of Spur, Texas, was a part of the Allied Forces. He was a Sergeant in the U.S. Infantry and was subsequently given a battlefield commission. He participated in the Battle of the Bulge, the largest and most deadly battle of the European Theatre, where he was killed in the winter of 1944-45. This was a six-week-long battle and there were 180,000 American and German casualties sustained in that epic struggle. Hub was ultimately buried at the U.S. Military Cemetery at Henri-Chapelle near Liège, Belgium, along with 8,000 other U.S. military. At my first opportunity I went to Belgium and visited his gravesite, and sent my mom and grandmother photos of the site.

Visiting Normandy and Henri-Chapelle at an early age in my life made a lasting impression on me and awakened a sense of patriotism and appreciation of freedom that has been with me throughout my life.

First Martini

There were two others doctors at the hospital besides myself - Lt Colonel Larry Loftus from California, an internist and hospital CEO, and Captain Bob Brannon, from Ohio, who had just completed his internship, as I had. Shortly after we got settled in, Dr. Loftus asked us over to his apartment for drinks and hors d'oeuvres. He made a batch of martinis, and I wasn't even sure what a martini was, and certainly had never drunk one. It was made with gin and I could hardly drink it.

I thought it tasted like shaving lotion. Having been raised in the "dry" town of Sudan, I had very little opportunity to develop a taste for any type of alcohol, but I managed to get through the evening, although a bit woozy. However, I must confess that after two years of living and dining in Paris, I did learn to appreciate the French wines.

President Eisenhower - Revisited

A few months after we arrived, our hospital received a call from Washington that President "Ike" Eisenhower was coming to Paris for a NATO/SHAPE conference. Paris was the headquarters of these organizations following World War II. We were asked to provide medical backup for him for any possible medical emergency that might arise while he was in attendance.

So, we had to import a cardiologist, a trauma surgeon and the like to be present while he was here, and we had an ambulance on call 24/7 and one of us three doctors was available for any contingent emergency. Suddenly it occurred to me, and I thought to myself, "Was this the reason I was sent to this highly strategic hospital?-- Because of my presence and activity at Fitzsimmons Army Hospital in Denver when President Eisenhower was hospitalized there the prior year?" I never asked...... I never knew....... and to this day........ I still don't know. While he was there for the few days for this NATO/SHAPE meeting we took turns on the ambulance duty, and fortunately we had no untoward events at any time.

NATO Commander – General Lauris Norstad

General Lauris Norstad was Supreme Allied Commander in Europe from 1956-62. We had several interactions with him during my tour of duty in Paris from 1956-58. He came to our hospital for regular checkups and for laboratory and X-ray tests. During his time as NATO Commander he championed the strengthening of allied military capabilities to act as a deterrent to enemy forces, particularly the Soviet Union. Other notables that we treated at our facility included John Foster Dulles, Secretary of State in the Eisenhower Administration; Senator Estes Kefauver, of Tennessee; General Curtis LeMay, head of SAC (Strategic Air Command) and his hunting partner, entertainer Arthur Godfrey. The latter two stopped off in Paris on their way to Africa for wild game hunting on two occasions while I was there.

General Charles de Gaulle

As I look back on those two years in and amongst the French people, I can deeply appreciate their rich history and tradition. Most of my friends who have visited France think of them as arrogant and impulsive, but I found them, on the whole, warm and caring. Early one morning I was awakened by some of my neighbors and I could tell they were extremely upset about something. They very hurriedly rushed me outside to the concrete fence surrounding my house and pointed out that someone had painted dozens of large crosses of Lorraine all along the fence. The Cross of Lorraine, which always reminded me of the Double T of Texas Tech University but with a shorter upper crossbar, was originally a symbol of Joan of Arc that later became also the symbol for the Free French Forces under General Charles de Gaulle.

There was a lot of political unrest during my years in France with three different Premieres elected during that time. My home was just a few blocks from Communist headquarters, and they vigorously opposed General de Gaulle's continually rising political influence (he later became president in 1959). My French neighbors were afraid the communists in the little village of Savigny-sur-Orge where I lived would think I was a de Gaulle supporter and do me harm, so they very dutifully helped me for several hours that morning wash off all the crosses of Lorraine.

The political situation got so troubling and intense at times, that those of us who lived out in the local French economy (and there weren't too many of us as most lived on base) were ordered to not wear our uniforms and to dress in casual civilian clothing and always travel in twos or threes to and from the air base. Fortunately, we never experienced any untoward events, but we were constantly on the lookout for anything remotely suspicious that might precipitate any trouble of any kind.

Black Market Gasoline – Monsieur Komeda

Our French home was heated by an old coal-burning furnace in the basement, as I mentioned earlier, and during one period of time that lasted for several months I was unable to purchase coal, as the Suez Canal was closed, producing a coal shortage in France. It is terribly damp and cold in Paris in the winter, and I went to the base commander's office seeking assistance and was told that since I opted to live on French economy housing off base, they couldn't help me and I would just have to figure it out for myself.

Well, early on I had met a Czechoslovakian friend, Monsieur Komeda, a former head of the Czech Red Cross, who spoke fluent French. He would do odd jobs for me and I would pay him with coffee and cigarettes, which were hard to come by for him.

He knew the local coal dealer and worked out a bartering deal with him that if I would supply the coal dealer with gasoline, he would supply me with coal. So, once a week I would fill up my car with gasoline from the air base gas station (as a doctor I was not rationed), and come home and siphon off 5 gallons of gasoline into a "Jerry can" (which it was called in those days). At the end of the month when I had four Jerry cans (20 gallons), Monsieur Komeda and I would sneak into the coal yard at night and leave off the gasoline, and the next day I would be delivered a ton of coal. We would actually signal with a flashlight from the top of a hill overlooking the coal yard, and on receipt of a similar signal from the coal yard, coast down the hill with headlights off to drop off the merchandise. This, of course, was an illegal transaction, but unfortunately I knew of no other way to heat my home for my family, and fortunately I was not ever caught during the several months this went on. I will always be grateful to Monsieur Komeda for helping me survive in a foreign country and also grateful for my early years of siphoning experience on the Nix farm in Sudan.

Most of my French neighbors stayed warm in the winter by wearing wool sweaters and drinking wine. They used coal furnaces for heat as I did, but their usage of coal paled in comparison to what I used. Every week we would put our coal ashes outside by the road to be picked up. My neighbors would have a small bucket of ashes containing maybe a couple of gallons and I would have this huge 50-gallon drum full. I was extremely embarrassed about this and over time learned the

French custom – more wine and less coal!

American Church in Paris

I had several other memorable experiences in France. One was serving on the Board of Deacons for two years at the American Church in Paris, a beautiful 200-year-old church located on the Seine River at 65, Quai d' Orsay. This is a nondenominational protestant church where services for Americans were held every Sunday throughout both World Wars. It is interesting to note that during the second World War the Germans, who occupied the Parish house, allowed the continuation of services attended by elderly Americans and British residents. Services were held in English and prayers for the President of the United States were offered every Sunday morning.

Numerous U.S. Presidents, including Ulysses S. Grant, Theodore Roosevelt and Woodrow Wilson, and other dignitaries such as Dr. Billy Graham have worshiped there, and I had a wonderful religious and spiritual experience there for two years.

American Hospital in Paris

Another historic landmark in Paris that I had the opportunity to work in is the American Hospital of Paris. During the time I was there it was one-half French civilian and the other half was U.S. military, and they shared laboratory and X-ray facilities and services.

We did not have the capability for any major surgery at my hospital at Orly Airfield, so when I encountered a patient that needed major surgical intervention, I would accompany the patient to the American Hospital and assist the Army Colonel surgeon with the surgery. I think these experiences helped solidify my thinking that I wanted to specialize in surgery when I was discharged from the Air Force.

The American Hospital of Paris, now all civilian, is the only civilian hospital in Europe that meets the accreditation standards of the Joint Commission of Accreditation of Healthcare Organizations (JACHO) under its rigorous American standards. I have had the opportunity to visit there again on a couple of other occasions since I left. A few years ago one of my granddaughters was hospitalized there when she became very ill while visiting in Europe. When my daughter called me from Spain about my granddaughter's illness I advised her to get to Paris as fast as she could and take her to the American Hospital there in NeuillyS/Seine. She did just that and I called the hospital, where I still have some contacts, and helped her make the arrangements. She was hospitalized there for several days, received outstanding care and subsequently made the trip back to the States without difficulty.

I always tell my friends who are going to Europe that if they become ill, they should make their way as quickly as possible to this hospital, which has over 500 physicians on the staff in every major medical and surgical specialty, all of whom speak fluent English.

Major Airline Crashes

We had two major airline crashes at Orly Airfield during my tour of duty – the first, an Air Italia plane the first year, and the second the next year, an Air France plane. They both occurred at night in bad weather. The USAF had a contract with the French government that through our hospital and staff we would provide for all air emergencies that might occur at Orly Airfield. It was not uncommon for us to make a call out to the flight line with an ambulance and staff, but most of these were precautionary and didn't amount to anything.

But these two were horrific, mass casualty events, and my first encounters with a disaster and trauma of this magnitude. In medical school and during my internship I'd seen quite a number of gunshot wounds and car accidents, but nothing on the scale of these two terrible accidents.

On both events, I was summoned out to the hospital by the French ambulance driver who came to my house with the message, "Dr. Salem, come quickly, major airline crash." For two years I'd tried unsuccessfully to get a telephone, but being a U.S. citizen, even though in the military in France, I was placed at the bottom of the list and never got a telephone. So when I was urgently needed at the hospital, this is how I was notified.

On arrival at the crash site of the Air France plane, emergency efforts were already under way. We employed several French men and women at our hospital and they had already been called out. I gave emergency care at the scene to some and then we transferred other survivors to our hospital for evaluation and treatment. Since we were not staffed at our hospital to do major trauma surgery, our main function was triage, evaluate and stabilize the patients, and then get them transferred to the appropriate hospitals in Paris. The problem of treatment was, of course, magnified many fold by the language barrier. Most of the passengers on the plane were French and only a few of them spoke English. But all of our French employees who worked at our hospital spoke fluent English and were of enormous help in our evaluation and management of the traumatized victims and getting them transferred to other hospitals in Paris.

Although our assistance may have been just part of a day's work, it did not go unnoticed. We were praised in Paris newspapers. To quote the article in the European edition of *The Stars & Stripes,* "Two doctors, Capt. Robert Salem and Capt. Robert Brannon, corpsmen and nurses, worked throughout much of the night giving emergency treatment," and I might have added "so did a number of our French secretaries."

Following the earlier Italian Airline crash, the Italian Consul General in Paris wrote to our base Commander, "Please extend my expression of deep gratitude to all ranks of your group who have done their utmost to save the lives and property of the passengers. Even if their efforts have not been repaid, they will long be remembered by all concerned as a magnificent example of human brotherhood and courage." After reading this article and seeing my picture in a Parisian newspaper, this only punctuated my lifelong dream of being a physician and rendering help to those in need, and ultimately to become a surgeon to enhance that capability.

Airmen in Distress
Late one night when I was on duty at our hospital, I was summoned to see one of our airmen who had been injured in an automobile accident and had been hospitalized at a small French hospital about an hour and a half from our airbase. It was a cold, damp and dreary evening, and as we approached the hospital it was apparent that there were no lights on, and all the lighting was being supplied by candlelight and flashlights. There was apparently no auxiliary power working and the whole scene

gave one a disquieting, eerie feeling. This lack of power was pretty common in France in those days. Everything was socialized and when they desired, all the workers would just go on strike and render an area with no power, even some rural hospitals. Consequently we always had candles and flashlights handy at our home. When I examined the airman by flashlight I could immediately determine that he was in severe, acute respiratory distress, and anoxic, and probably needed a tracheotomy. But to attempt such a procedure under those conditions with no light or suction, I thought it would result in a tragic event. So I found the largest bore needle I could find and inserted it into his airway through the cricothyroid membrane, the soft spot of the neck just below the Adam's apple. This afforded him enough improvement in his breathing that I could load him in our ambulance and take him back to our hospital in Paris where I then did a formal tracheotomy and inserted a chest tube because of multiple rib fractures that had caused a pneumothorax. He subsequently recovered from this ordeal without any complications and for many years thereafter, I always carried one of those needles in my billfold in the event of another such emergency.

On one other occasion I saw another airman at our hospital clinic with cough, shortness of breath and chest pain. When I took his shirt off to examine his chest, I noted these peculiar red rings about an inch in diameter all over the front and back of his chest. And I said to myself, "Well, I must have slept through that lecture in medical school because I sure don't remember a disease entity manifested by anything as peculiar as this." On further questioning of the airman's French wife, she told me that she had taken her husband to see a French country doctor for his symptoms and he had treated him by applying multiple little suction devices to his chest wall. These were little small suction cups with a glass component and one would swab the inside of the glass part with alcohol, light it with a match, which would then create heat and warmth, and then you would squeeze the little bulb attached to create a suction effect and then place it on the chest wall where it would stay attached for several minutes at a time. This procedure was designed to "draw out" the infection in the lung – "Le Grippe" they called it. This was just one of several of these cases that I saw over the two years I was there, and an example of how different and far behind medicine was in France in those days compared to what we had in the States.

"Le Grippe"

I am sick with "The Grip"!
"Le Grippe"! "Le Grippe"!
Not the soft leather kind
You may have in your mind.
But the kind that takes hold
In a way can't be told,
From the head to the feet
The pain is complete!

Of all diseases on earth
Since old Adam's birth
"The Grip" beats them all.
It's the devil's own call
I know cause I've got it.
It's down right despotic
It has it's own way,
It's no use to pray
"Special Prayers" do not count
Nor reduce the amount
Of torture and pain
In this wonderful frame.

The only thing we can do,
Get a doctor or two,
He will feel of your pulse
And watch the result.
If your heart is all right
He then will look bright –
For the heart is the life
In these poor bodies of strife.

He'll look you all through
From your head to your shoe,
Your liver and throat
And organs remote –
Your stomach and gall

He'll surely find all.
Then leave you some pills, and
Without nonsense or frills
He'll declare with a vim
That unless something "sets in"
You are bound to get well.
But how can he tell?
Of one thing I'm sure,
"Le Grippe" is near hell!
Dr. S.L.G. Crane
June 13, 1908

London – Sir William Harvey

An intern colleague of mine from Fitzsimmons Army Hospital in Denver was stationed in Italy, and he called me one day and said that he was going to attend a medical meeting in London in a few weeks and wanted to know if I might could meet him there to reminisce over our experiences. He informed me that the meeting was sponsored by the Royal College of Surgeons, commemorating the tercentenary of the death of William Harvey. Mr. Harvey was an English physician who first discovered the circulation of the blood and the function of the heart as a pump propelling blood throughout the body in 1628. He died in 1657 and thus this meeting in London in 1957 was celebrating the 300th year following his death.

I immediately contacted the office of the Secretary of the Royal College of Surgeons and asked them if I might attend the meeting. They were most accommodating and sent me a special invitation asking for Captain Doctor Robert Salem to attend this very special meeting sponsored by the Royal College of Surgeons. When I received the invitation I immediately ran over to our headquarters and said, "Say, guys, look what I've received." They were so impressed that they issued me TDY (temporary duty) orders to attend the meeting for a week and compensated me TDY pay in addition to my regular officers' pay. Drs. Loftus and Brannon at my hospital were not as impressed and were quite envious, and when I hopped on one of our C47 Gooney Birds for a flight over the channel to London, they came out to the tarmac with a dozen red roses for me to put on William Harvey's gravesite. I hooked up with my intern friend in London and we enjoyed the hospitality of the Royal College of Surgeons for several days.

"Gooney Birds" (C-47-DC3) – Flights

The DC3, nicknamed the "Gooney Bird" was one of the most durable and versatile airplanes in the history of air travel. It was mass produced during WW II as a utility transport, but used in all imaginable roles. Besides its use as a personnel and flight transport, it was also used as a glider tug and air ambulance, and was active in all theaters of WW II, especially during the "D-Day" landings in Normandy.

Wiesbaden

We had several of these aircraft at our airbase and used them for a variety of flying missions. I once had a flight on one of ours configured as an air ambulance, as a patient. One night I was flown on a litter to the USAF main hospital in Wiesbaden, Germany, which was the headquarters of the USAF in Europe at the time. I had had a severe lumbar disc problem that had not responded to the usual conservative treatment and it was felt I needed to see a neurosurgeon. The only one in the USAF in Europe was stationed at the headquarters hospital in Wiesbaden.

So, I was put on a litter for transport and off we went from Paris to Wiesbaden, taking off in a rain storm. It was a horribly turbulent ride, but the steady, durable Gooney Bird got us there safely and I was evaluated by the neurosurgeon, who felt that I probably needed to have a myelogram and most probably would need surgery. But I was just a few weeks from completing my tour of duty and starting my residency, and I knew that if I had done what he recommended I would not be able to start my surgical residency with Dr. DeBakey, and would miss the opportunity of a lifetime. So, I declined the treatment offer and had to sign all sorts of waivers and flew back to Paris subsequently and ultimately started my residency with back pain, which intermittently plagued me throughout my career.

Berlin

After the allied victory in WW II, Germany was divided into four zones occupied by the four power nations: United States, United Kingdom, France and the Soviet Union. The western zone was occupied by the Allied Forces (US, UK and France), and the east zone was occupied by the Soviet Union. The capital of West Germany was located in Bonn and the capital of the eastern zone was located in East Berlin. So Germany itself was divided geographically into an east and west, and likewise, Berlin was divided into an east and a west, with East Berlin occupied by the Soviet Union and West Berlin occupied by the Allied Forces. Additionally, there were three West Berlin air corridors established to be used exclusively by western allies flying between West Germany and West Berlin. These regulated airways controlled all military and civil air traffic, passing over East Germany and going on into West Berlin. The air spaces within these corridors were for the exclusive use of the US, UK and French registered noncombat aircraft belonging to these countries' armed forces and airlines operated by pilots holding those countries' passports.

I made two Gooney Bird flights from Paris to West Berlin landing at Tempelhof Airbase in West Berlin. Our navigators were especially diligent in making certain that we did not stray outside our designated air corridor, particularly over East Germany, where if we strayed out of our corridor, we would immediately be accompanied by Soviet MIGs and forced to land at best, or worse-case scenario, would be shot down.

On two other occasions I went to Berlin to a medical meeting by a military train. I drove from Paris to Frankfurt, Germany, where the train left for Berlin. It was a Pullman sleeper train and only traveled at night, leaving about 6 p.m. and arriving around 8 a.m. the next day in West Berlin. About 2 a.m. the train made an obligatory stop at the East German/West German border. Once we were stopped for inspection, the train was immediately surrounded by Russians with automatic weapons drawn. We had been told never to give up our passports and always keep them in our possession, but on this trip the Russians came by our rooms demanding that we give them our passports. Momentarily I pondered what to do, but after another second stern request and looking down the muzzle of a rifle I surrendered my passport, hoping and praying I had made the right decision. We were delayed for two to three hours, why

I don't know, but eventually our passports were returned to us and we traveled on to Berlin without incident. I had the opportunity to visit East Berlin while I was there, and the difference between East and West Berlin was stark and astonishing. This was 10 years after WW II had ended and the western sector of Berlin was already undergoing major rebuilding and modernization, whereas the eastern sector under Russian and Communist control still looked like a freshly bombed-out city. I had studied two years of German at Texas Tech and had the opportunity on this and other trips to Germany to practice my German, but I think I did a better job with the conversational French that I picked up in France over German.

Geneva

We had many other Gooney Bird flights to Geneva, Switzerland. We were paid monthly in what we called "paper money" which was military dollars at the time, and then we would exchange those for U.S. dollars. We found out that we could get more French francs for our U.S. dollars in Switzerland than we could in Paris. So, frequently, we would take up a big collection from all of the airmen and officers on the base and take a big sack full of U.S. dollars to Geneva where we exchanged them into French francs, getting about 10 percent more French francs than we could in Paris.

I loved flying to Geneva. It is considered to be one of the leading financial centers in the world, and these financial institutions took care of our sacks of U.S. dollars with haste and dispatch. It is a worldwide center for diplomacy and the site of numerous international organizations, such as the United Nations and the Red Cross. It has an antiquity dating back to 100 B.C. and has many old historic sites. Situated by Lake Geneva and surrounded by two mountain chains, the Alps and the Jura, it is one of my favorite cities in Europe.

Marseilles

We also made regular flights to Marseilles on the southern coast of France where we had an air base and airmen there. Regularly, we would take a doctor, a nurse and a dentist down to Marseilles and hold sick call there. We were able to take care of most of their medical and dental needs at the time, but occasionally some were sick enough to come back and be hospitalized, but this was also an enjoyable experience flying down in those sturdy old C-47s. Marseille is a beautiful city located on the southeast coast of France, on the Mediterranean, and is France's third largest city, after Paris and Lyon. It is France's oldest city and its largest commercial port. Because of its mild Mediterranean climate, it is a popular city for tourists. With its rugged, scenic coastline and mountainous background, I could have easily spent more time there. I did, however, have some time to visit some of the many historic sites in the city.

From "Ike" (Dwight Eisenhower) To "Mike" (Dr. Michael E. Debakey)

I had many other trips in the Gooney Birds to North Africa and other destinations in Europe, but one day as my duty in Europe was about to end, I received a letter from Dr. Michael E. DeBakey, Chairman of the Department of Surgery, Baylor College of Medicine in Houston, Texas, which indicated that I had been accepted into the surgical training program there in Houston. This was the beginning of a new chapter and the continuation of the "DeBakey Factor" in my life and the start of a relationship that would factor into my life for the next 50 years. So, from "Ike" Eisenhower in Paris, France, I was soon off to "Mike" DeBakey and surgical training in Houston, Texas.

Henri-Chapelle American Cemetery and Memorial

American Battle Monuments Commission

Aunt Dora Hyatt (widow of Lt. Hub Hyatt)
and Betty Salem Korioth

Charles de Gaulle

Cross of Lorraine

General Lauris Norstad —
Commander of NATO

Centennial Program

The American Church in Paris

65, Quai d'Orsay, 7e
PARIS, FRANCE

1857 - 1957

Orly Airmen: Friends in Need

By DON WALTER, Staff Writer

IT WAS A QUIET night at the 7415th USAF dispensary at Paris' Orly Field—there were only two or three patients in the wards and physicians had completed their rounds for the evening.

It was 8:25 pm.

All was in order, too, over at the 7415th AB Gp's fire department. The day's work was finished. Fire hoses had been inspected. The big trucks had been washed and backed into their places. The night crew had come on duty.

Transient airmen were waiting in the military terminal for their flights to be announced. Some Wafs were having coffee. Then a flash, followed by a bang. A plane had crashed, and it was on fire.

Three minutes later air base firemen were on the scene. It was the second time within the past three months that Orly airmen had demonstrated the speed with which they could come to the rescue in time of need.

The ill-fated plane had crashed on the field just off the runway, it was later determined, as a result of fog. Seconds before the crash, one night last month, it had been a sleek French-built Armagnac, four-engined airliner resembling a DC6, in service between Tunis and Paris. There were 57 passengers and a crew of nine aboard.

What could have ended in great loss of life was averted by the Orly Field civilian fire department, aided by the base fire fighters. The blaze was extinguished within a few minutes, allowing rescuers to remove the injured.

At the same moment the fire trucks roared out of their garage, four AF ambulances hurried to the crash. Although some passengers were pinned within the wreckage and could not be freed for some time, most were able to escape through a huge crack in the fuselage of the plane.

Nearly all were injured in varying degrees. The 12 most seriously hurt were taken to the base dispensary for care. Two doctors, Capt Robert Salem and Capt Robert Brannon, corpsmen and nurses worked through much of the night giving emergency treatment. The victims later were transferred to civilian hospitals.

Partially as a result of the cooperation of the Orly airmen, death toll in the Armagnac crash was kept to a minimum. There was only one fatality.

The Orly disaster followed a less fortunate accident last November. That time fire and medical crews were called to another crash and reached the spot only minutes after it occurred. It was an Italian airliner bound for New York with 35 aboard, which had crashed shortly after takeoff, plunging into a village.

But only two passengers were saved. The plane had hit two houses, demolishing them and setting a third on fire. Snow had fallen. The temperature was near freezing. Orly airmen, working beside French firefighters, kept the fire from spreading to other houses.

In both cases the real thing was almost like a dry run for the 7415th fire department and dispensary personnel. Extensive training and regular drills keep these men fit should their services be required when an AF plane is in trouble or a civilian disaster requires their cooperation.

And although their assistance may have been just part of the day's work, it did not go unnoticed. They were praised in Paris newspapers. After the November crash Italian Consul General in Paris Ettore Baistrocchi wrote to the base commander, Lt Col R. A. Wilson:

"Please extend my expression of deep gratitude to all ranks of your group who have done their utmost to save the lives and property of the passengers. Even if their efforts have not been fully repaid they will long be remembered by all concerned as a magnificent example of human brotherhood and courage."

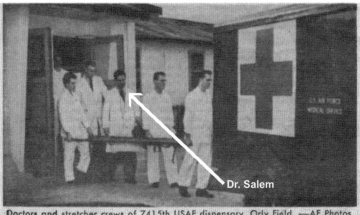

Doctors and stretcher crews of 7415th USAF dispensary, Orly Field. —AF Photos

Dr. Salem

RDF190

~~RFW UW1088 AB D HSD293 FAX~~

HOUSTON TEX 76 4 1409

LT ROBERT J SALEM CAPT USAF (MC)

7415TH USA DISPENSARY APO 230 PARIS (FRANCE)

PLEASED TO INFORM OF YOUR ACCEPTANCE AS FIRST YEAR

RESIDENT IN GENERAL SURGERY AT THE BAYLOR UNIVERSITY

COLLEGE OF MEDICINE AFFILIATED HOSPITALS FOR ONE YEAR

BEGINNING JULY 1 1958 WITH RENEWAL CONTINGENT UPON

SATISFACTORY PERFORMANCE PLEASE REPLY IMMEDIATELY WHETHER

YOU WISH TO ACCEPT WE LOOK FORWARD TO HAVING YOU

WITH US

    MICHAEL E DEBAKEY MD CHAIRMAN RESIDENCY PROGRAM

    COMMITTEE FOR GENERAL SURGERY

BAYLOR UNIVERSITY
COLLEGE OF MEDICINE
AFFILIATED HOSPITALS RESIDENCY PROGRAM
TEXAS MEDICAL CENTER
HOUSTON, TEXAS

BAYLOR UNIVERSITY COLLEGE OF MEDICINE
JEFFERSON DAVIS HOSPITAL
METHODIST HOSPITAL
TEXAS CHILDREN'S HOSPITAL
VETERANS ADMINISTRATION HOSPITAL

TELEPHONE JA 9-4951

November 27, 1957

AIR MAIL

Dr. Robert J. Salem
7415th USAF Dispensary
APO 230, New York, N. Y.

Dear Doctor Salem:

I am pleased to acknowledge your acceptance of the appointment offered you as resident in general surgery at the Baylor University College of Medicine Affiliated Hospitals.

In confirmation of my wire, this appointment will be as a first year resident in general surgery for a period of one year beginning July 1, 1958, with renewal contingent upon satisfactory performance. Hospital contracts will be arranged later.

We are looking forward to having you with us.

Yours sincerely,

Michael E. DeBakey, M. D., Chairman
Residency Program Committee
for General Surgery

MED:mn
Enc.

"Gooney Bird" - DC-3, C-47

51

6

HOUSTON, TEXAS
BAYLOR COLLEGE OF MEDICINE RESIDENCY

I had certainly heard of Dr. DeBakey, but having been out of the country for two years, I had had no recent discussions with anyone about him other than with one lady, Pete Florian—her parents had expected a boy but when she arrived, they decided to keep the name of "Pete". I just by accident one day in Paris ran into her and her husband, who was a businessman, and learned that she was a nurse anesthetist and had worked at Methodist Hospital in Houston with Dr. DeBakey. She was so enamored with him and all of the great pioneering work he was doing in the field of cardiovascular surgery that she strongly encouraged me to go there for my training. I think she actually was the person that most influenced me in making an application for my surgical training there, and I didn't know for sure, but may have had some influence with Dr. DeBakey accepting me, as I had had no opportunity for a personal interview, being stationed overseas in Paris.

I wanted to make a good impression on my first day beginning my surgical residency, so I arrived at what I thought would be an early time at 6 a.m. and was promptly reprimanded and informed that surgical ward rounds began at 4 a.m. So, that was the inauspicious beginning of a rather tumultuous and rigorous four years of surgical training.

To compound the physically and mentally demanding schedule, my compensation for working over 100 hours per week was the hefty sum of $25 per month. Well, I wasn't to despair because each year I got a $25 per month raise so that my fourth year I was paid $100 per month.

In any event, as I began my surgical training there, I didn't realize or appreciate the fact that I was starting my training at the place and time of the beginning of the modern era of cardiovascular surgery, and that the person to be later known as the "Father of Modern Cardiovascular Surgery" and probably the most renowned surgeon and physician of the 20th Century, was none other than my chief, Dr. Michael DeBakey. As I started in 1958, there was another surgeon who Dr. DeBakey had recruited to join him who served as Vice Chairman of the Department of Surgery, Dr. Denton A. Cooley. Dr. Cooley would work with Dr.

DeBakey for several years in the Department of Surgery and then later would separate and establish the celebrated Texas Heart Institute and become equally as famous as Dr. DeBakey. So, I had the unique opportunity of working with two of the most prominent cardiovascular surgeons in the annals of surgery.

I was initiated into the field of vascular surgery almost from the very first day of my residency. Synthetic vascular grafts for the by-pass of obstructed arteries or to replace arterial aneurysms had been developed in the 1950s, led by Dr. DeBakey's intuitive genius. The initial grafts were quite porous and consequently surgery to resect an abdominal aortic aneurysm, e.g., was associated with a tremendous amount of blood loss. On a typical surgery of this kind, we would routinely have five to six units of blood available for the inevitable intra operative transfusions always needed during the operative procedure. We would have at least two or three IVs placed to administer the blood and other IV fluids and medications.

During resection of an abdominal aortic aneurysm, the circulation above and below the aneurysm is clamped off with specialized non traumatic vascular clamps. Once the aneurysm has been resected and the synthetic graft sewn in, the real drama begins. Before the vascular clamps are released to restore circulation through the graft, we would pack the area around and on top of the graft with multiple absorbent laparotomy pads and then all four or five of us scrubbed in would put both hands down, with fingers spread, on the lap pads as the clamps were released. Inevitably and even with eight to ten hands applying extreme pressure, we would gradually see this huge tide of fresh blood rapidly saturate the pads and fill the abdominal cavity and spill over the sides of the patient onto the floor. All the while, we were pumping in blood through two ports as fast as we could and giving medications to prevent shock from occurring. After a few minutes of this spine-tingling experience, the crisis was over, the bleeding ceased.... and all was well.

After the first one of these procedures I participated in, I thought to myself, "My God, are these guys trying to kill this patient or help him?" But over time as newer synthetic grafts were developed, they became much less porous and today in most cases an abdominal aortic aneurysm resection can be accomplished without the necessity of a single blood transfusion. The courage of these early surgical pioneers like Dr. DeBakey to forge ahead with these high risk operations that no one had ever done before is truly remarkable.

Dr. Denton A. Cooley

Dr. Cooley and Dr. DeBakey had very different personalities and these two great surgeons became temperamentally incompatible, thus prompting Dr. Cooley to ultimately move across the street where he founded the Texas Heart Institute.

Dr. Cooley's fame spread throughout the '60s as he applied his extraordinary dexterity to surgery on hearts of infants with congenital heart ailments and he also became internationally renowned for the development of artificial heart valves.

While my personal contacts and interaction through the years have been primarily with Dr. DeBakey, Dr. Cooley remains in my mind and my personal relationships with him, a towering, unique figure in the Cardiovascular Surgical world and a surgeon of equal stature to Dr. DeBakey, an icon and legendary giant in his own right.

I remember once assisting Dr. Cooley and some little minor mishap occurred, and unlike Dr. DeBakey, Dr. Cooley's demeanor was much more controlled and deliberate whereas, under a similar scenario, Dr. DeBakey would react more vociferously and animated. Dr. Cooley reacted with, "Well, Dr. Salem, if you don't know how to do this, just tell me and I'll do it myself." I can assure you that the next time I scrubbed with him, I boned up on every aspect of the case because I didn't want to experience any more penetrating and demeaning remarks like that again.

Everyone with whom I have talked who has scrubbed with both surgeons feels that Dr. Cooley has the most superb surgical technique in the world. The fine, delicate finger movements of his hands are unparalleled by anyone and to some degree, at least, can be attributable to his working on tiny infants with complicated congenital heart defects.

Dr. Michael DeBakey

Dr. DeBakey was the most intense, focused and hard-working person I've ever known – superhuman – almost inhuman – never slept more than three hours per night and the ultimate perfectionist, and the personification of excellence in everything he did. He expected and demanded even more from his residents, and held his residents accountable for all complications, all untoward events and even for Acts of God. He was known to have fired a resident on the spot for something less than a perfect outcome, so that we lived and worked in constant fear that something would happen that would hasten our departure from the program.

Every one of us who worked side by side with him stood in utter awe and bewilderment as to his incomparable stamina, drive and intensity. He taught by example and among the many things he taught us, two things stand out uppermost in my mind. The first is his total commitment to excellence and perfection – every detail must be well thought out – every movement of the hands must be purposeful, and every stitch must be perfectly placed. Anything short of absolute perfection was simply not acceptable. The second thing I learned from Dr. DeBakey was what a "hard work" ethic really meant. Twenty hour days were the norm and frequently they were twenty-two and not uncommonly, twenty-four-- and the next day was a work day as well. Many times during my career I have drawn on that experience to perform yet another operation when I was so dog tired I didn't think I could. I would always think and recall, "Well, if that son-of-a-gun can do it without much sleep then so can I."

DeBakey Anecdotes

After a few days on his service, sleeping two to three hours a day at 30-minute intervals, I told one of his staff surgeons that I didn't think I had the physical or mental stamina to go on. He said to me, "Bob, just hang in there another day. Dr. DeBakey can't possibly keep this pace up either and he'll probably drop dead tomorrow." So, I lived those four years one day at a time, thinking each day, "Today's the day – he's going to drop dead and I can go home and get some sleep". Forty years later, he was still keeping up that same torrid pace and hectic, almost inhuman schedule.

I remember commenting to some of my colleagues, soaked in blood following a night of an unusual amount of trauma and no sleep

56

at Jefferson Davis Hospital (later to become Ben Taub), that just a few weeks ago I was an officer and a gentleman in the USAF in beautiful Paris, and look at me now, a slave laborer making less than $1 a day.

In the presence of Kings and Queens, Heads of State, Presidents, movie stars and other dignitaries, Dr. DeBakey was the most charming person imaginable, but for his residents working with him it could be an excruciatingly harrowing experience at times. His demeanor in the operating room was intensely demanding, frequently demeaning and spiced with highly charged and lively animation. Once as I was assisting him on a surgical procedure, some little minor thing occurred and he laid down his dissecting scissors, raised his arms above his head, looked up into the ceiling and wailed, "Oh God, why are you persecuting me, you've surrounded me with imbeciles." On another occasion he said, "You know Dr. Salem, if I had three hands I wouldn't even need you."

On still another occasion when I was assisting him, I was holding a retractor to enhance his exposure of the operative field. He squeezed my fingers so hard against the sharp edge of the retractor handle trying to get more exposure that I developed a temporary nerve injury on the inner side of my left index finger (digital nerve palsy) that lasted for several months. I dared not complain to him for fear of incurring more of his ire.

On yet another occasion he was making ward rounds on a patient on whom he had done an abdominal aortic aneurysm resection. The patient had developed some rectal bleeding on the second day following surgery, and not knowing otherwise, I was proctoscoping the patient trying to identify the source of the bleeding. When he came by he said, "What in the hell are you doing?" I said, "Dr. DeBakey, I'm trying to find out where this patient is bleeding from." He said, "Give me that scope and let me show you where to stick it." He meant, of course, "up mine!" Later, I learned that patients undergoing this type of surgery frequently will have some temporary bleeding from the left side of the colon, where a blood vessel supplying that segment of the colon is automatically divided in the course of the operation, but this was a self-limited process and invariably stopped on its own accord without doing anything. This was a hard lesson to learn, but one I remembered for the rest of my career.

Any resident or fellow who has trained with Dr. DeBakey will have countless other similar stories of this nature. If anyone hears anecdotally of any of these stories, let me assure you they're all true.

Disaster in the OR

It was about a month before the end of my four years of training when another catastrophic event occurred that almost shattered my life. As chief resident I was feeling pretty good – had survived three years and eleven months of the most rigorous training anywhere in the world and had survived many "close calls" with Dr. DeBakey, and was feeling very secure and confident with my surgical abilities. I just had one more major case of Dr. DeBakey's to get behind me and then I was "out of the woods" and back to Lubbock, Texas. Dr. DeBakey had scheduled a heart valve replacement surgery that afternoon, which was to be the first heart valve operation ever done at the old city/county hospital, Jefferson Davis (later to become Ben Taub), on a patient from Dr. DeBakey's hometown of Lake Charles, Louisiana. I had been in contact for several hours with the folks at Methodist Hospital, where he was doing several other operations that day, to be sure about what time we would finish over there and might arrive at Jeff Davis. He liked to have the preliminary part of the operation performed by staff and residents, and get ready for him to do just the main part or "meat" of the operative procedure. Time was so critical for him that we made every effort to be on time with every piece of the total effort.

So, when I learned about what time he would be arriving, we anesthetized the patient, made the chest incision, and had the patient on the heart/lung machine the moment he arrived. He hurriedly scrubbed in, opened up the heart and removed the diseased valve, and began sewing in the new valve. The Houston skies were cloudy that day and rain had been forecast, but no one had remotely considered what we were about to experience. We were about halfway through sewing in the new valve when the damndest and most severe lightning and thunderstorm hit the hospital area that you can imagine. After a sudden lightning strike nearby, the operating room went into total darkness. All auxiliary power, which is supposed to immediately come on in circumstances like this, and provide light and power, did not for some unknown reason, and I thought to myself, "Oh damn, this patient's going to die and I'm going

58

to get blamed for all of this. Dr. DeBakey's going to fire me today, one month short of completing my residency."

Well immediately the heart/lung technician began to pump the machine manually – these machines have a hand crank or pump that will effectively keep the blood circulating and provide proper oxygenation of the blood if there is a power outage. Then, other OR personnel rapidly found some flashlights and shined enough light into the heart valve area so that we could complete the valve replacement, sew up the heart, and get the patient off the heart/lung machine.

We all breathed a huge sigh of relief when the lights came back on, and the heart resumed normal function and activity, and by all appearances immediately postoperatively, the patient survived the operation without sustaining any obvious complications.

I then braced myself for the assault I knew was coming. Angrily he said, "Salem, come over here" as he was removing his gown and gloves. "Come with me and we're going to find those electricians and maintenance folks in the basement and find out why the hell our auxiliary power didn't come on, and get rid of those incompetents." And I said, "You bet, Dr. DeBakey, let's go find them" desperately wanting to keep his fury focused on those guys rather than on me because, as I noted earlier, residents can be held accountable for Acts of God and fired for lesser events than this.

So, we, in fact, did find the folks in charge of this area and there was, in fact, a change of personnel that day. This patient ultimately did well, but I didn't learn until many years later that the valve that I assisted Dr. DeBakey with that day began to malfunction (as some valves did in the early days of this type of surgery), and a few years later after that original surgery, Dr. Don Bricker, who was Chief of Surgery at Ben Taub, reoperated on the same patient and put in a newer valve and the patient did well again the second time – whew!

Another tragic event occurred with a patient of Dr. DeBakey's – a physician from South America. Dr. DeBakey had operated on him for a thoracic aortic aneurysm – one of the most challenging of surgical operations which fifty years ago was attended by a significant mortality and morbidity. I had not scrubbed with him on this particular case, but had the primary responsibility of taking care of him in the Surgical ICU postoperatively. At the time Dr. DeBakey left the country for a few days, the patient seemed to be doing reasonably well. However, in the middle of the night on about the fourth postoperative day, I was called by the head nurse of ICU to come and see the patient immediately as he had suddenly gone into profound shock.

Shortly after I arrived, the patient went into complete cardiac arrest and I rapidly determined that he was hemorrhaging from his surgical site. I immediately opened up his chest incision in the bed and found major hemorrhage from his thoracic aorta at the site where the synthetic graft had been sewn in. I put a vascular clamp on the aorta proximal to where the bleeding was coming from which stopped the hemorrhage. I then called the staff surgeon on-call who was covering for Dr. DeBakey and he immediately came in and we tried for several hours to save the patient, but were unsuccessful.

When Dr. DeBakey returned a couple of days later I had to inform him of what had transpired and he became enraged and began to confront me with remarks that implied that I was responsible for his death. The staff surgeon immediately came to my rescue and informed Dr. DeBakey that I had not even scrubbed in on the patient's surgery and had done everything humanly possible to save his life, whereupon Dr. DeBakey backed off.

On another similar occasion, another staff surgeon, Dr. Sam Henly, came to my rescue as well. Sam was a Lubbock native and began his surgical residency at Baylor with Dr. DeBakey a few years before I started. After his residency training, he stayed on the staff and practiced his entire career in Houston and has been an avid and loyal colleague of Dr. DeBakey's for more than 50 years.

In a recent reflection, he wrote in the Journal of the Methodist DeBakey Heart and Vascular Center about an incident when one Sunday morning Dr. Henly walked into the surgical offices at Baylor and he was alone with Dr. DeBakey who was seated at his desk when Dr. DeBakey asked Dr. Henly where everyone was, Dr. Henly replied that this was Sunday and he presumed that everyone was at church. Whereupon Dr. DeBakey responded with, "Well, why are they not here doing the Lord's work?" This was characteristic of Dr. DeBakey's entire life---constantly working ---24/7/365.

Dr. DeBakey was such a perfectionist and as Dr. Henly noted, loved his patients dearly and was severely affected when they did not do well after surgery. I think he had difficulty in accepting the fact, that, he, like everyone else doing surgery, had complications from time to time. He felt in his own mind I think, that since he had done everything perfectly, if the outcome was not perfect, that it therefore, must be someone else's fault. Unfortunately, every operation regardless of whom the surgeon is, is attended by a certain morbidity and mortality and the more difficult the operation and the more co-morbidities the patient has (e.g. obesity, diabetes, heart disease, age, etc.), the higher the numbers.

The pursuit of excellence was Dr. DeBakey's main objective in life and he tried to instill that principle in everyone with whom he worked – colleagues, staff and residents alike.

Giants in the OR

It would be several years later that I would fully appreciate the incredibly unique opportunity and experience that I had there at Baylor under the tutelage of Dr. DeBakey and Dr. Cooley, surrounded by the most incomparable staff of surgeons in the world – Dr. Stanley Crawford, Dr. George Morris, Dr. George Jordan, Dr. Ed Garrett, Dr. Arthur Beall, Dr. Francis Usher, and many others – all giants in their own right.

Stanley Crawford came to Baylor in 1954 from Massachusetts General and became the world's leading authority on the surgical treatment of thoraco-abdominal aneurysms – aneurysms that involve the chest and abdomen below the diaphragm.

George Morris was Dr. DeBakey's first surgical resident in 1950 and became renowned for his expertise in peripheral vascular disease entities as well as for renal artery bypass operations.

George Jordan was Mayo trained before he came to Baylor in 1952 and was known as the "G.I." surgeon. He was internationally known for his expertise on surgery of the pancreas.

Ed Garrett received acclaim for being a participant on some of the first coronary bypasses ever done in the early 60s.

Arthur Beall is best known for his lung surgery, development of artificial heart valves and working with the surgical residency program at Baylor.

Francis Usher was best known for his development of Marlex

Mesh, a synthetic material used in many types of hernia repairs.

Every one of these giants were at Baylor when I started my residency and it was my privilege and honor to have had the opportunity to assist and be assisted by each and every one of them on many occasions.

Junior Residents

I was also very fortunate as chief resident for Dr. DeBakey to have three outstanding junior residents – Dr. Don Bricker, Dr. George Noon and Dr. Charles McCollum - working under me. As we were escorting Dr. DeBakey from Houston to Lubbock one time a few years ago for him to give the inaugural Covenant Heart Institute – Michael E. DeBakey, MD, Distinguished Lectureship Program in 2004, I reminded Dr. DeBakey about whom my junior residents were that I had working under me at the time. He said, "Well, hell, Bob, with talent like that you must not have had much to do." Whereupon I said, "Yeah, right, Dr. DeBakey, with the help of Bricker, Noon and McCollum, I only had to work 20 hours a day instead of the usual 22."

M.D. Anderson Cancer Hospital

I also had a wonderful training experience during my residency at M.D. Anderson Cancer Hospital performing and assisting on many cancer surgical operations. I give tremendous credit to Dr. Richard Martin, Head of GI Surgery at M.D. Anderson at the time. Residents and fellows were not too plentiful back then, and I got to perform a tremendous number of operations with Dr. Martin assisting and instructing me, and then on the VIPs I assisted Dr. Martin. I had rotations on head and neck surgery whose chief at the time was Dr. Jay Ballantyne, as well as a very productive rotation on breast and thyroid surgery under Dr. Ed White, chairman of that section.

Goodbye, Dr. DeBakey

In spite of all the human indignities I felt I suffered during those four years, at the end of my training I felt as though I had received the best surgical training in the world – the incredible volume and variety of cases could not have been exceeded anywhere, and because of this I developed the confidence and experience I needed to tackle just about any general surgical or peripheral vascular case with which I might be confronted.

By tradition, the chief resident goes by the chief's office to pay his respects and say goodbye as he or she is leaving the training program, and to get an autographed picture of the chief. So, I went by his office to choose a picture as I was preparing to leave, and he was not in. His assistant said, "Well, Dr. Salem, let me just get him to sign his photo and you can come back tomorrow and see him and pick it up." I said, "That would be fine" whereupon she said, "Well, what would you like for him to say on the picture." I said that it didn't really matter, just to tell him to say whatever he liked. She said, "Well, what does he usually call you?" and jokingly I said, "Well, he usually calls me 'You GD Stupid Baboon' but I'd rather he not say that. I'd rather he just lie and say something nice" which he did as you can see from the photograph. So, I took his signed photograph and headed back to Lubbock, Texas, to practice the skills I had learned and the training I received under the "Texas Tornado," one of Dr. DeBakey's many nicknames. This was not the end of the "DeBakey Factor" in my life, however, as many exciting events with Dr. DeBakey were yet to unfold in my association with him.

Forty-five-years later, I still have his picture hanging on my wall.

Dr. Michael E. DeBakey

Dr. Michael E.
DeBakey
(Autographed Photo)

Dr. Denton A.
Cooley

I thought I had seen all of the sandstorms and eaten all of the sand that I wanted for the rest of my life, but in the final analysis, I guess I couldn't wait to get back to West Texas to start my surgical practice. Why? Because of the many old friends I had there, and the goodness and friendliness of West Texas people. West Texas folks were just different from any other people in the world that I had encountered in my journeys through many parts of the world. In my early experiences, living with other people in many other places made me realize what was important. Yes, we didn't have any mountains or lakes in West Texas, just dry land with sandstorms and tumbleweeds, but the wonderful people made up for the difference.

The opportunities of beginning a practice in Lubbock to initiate a program of blood vessel surgery were also very compelling. The volume of surgery of this type that I had had in my training was incredible and I was very confident I could perform this type of surgery well. Subsequently, I was pleasantly surprised to find that a climatic change had occurred in West Texas since I had left Sudan 16 years earlier – many fewer severe sandstorms, and one had to actually search to find a tumbleweed, but there were still a few to be seen tumbling along on a bad day.

Immediately upon arrival, now with a third daughter, Sharon, who was born a few months before I finished my residency, I had the hospital order us a supply of the necessary specialized blood vessel instruments, suture material and synthetic Dacron grafts used to replace or bypass diseased arteries.

I also had several physician friends from college and medical school who I felt would refer patients to me to help get my practice started quicker. In particular, there a group of physicians in Levelland, Texas - Drs. Joe Harrison, Andy Walsh, Jim Renegar and Dale Campbell, and others who were immediately supportive and began referring patients to me for surgery shortly after my arrival.

Another Memorable Appendectomy

Shortly after I arrived in Lubbock, I paid a visit to them in Levelland, and the receptionist informed me that two of them were in the operating room at the time doing some surgery. She called them in the OR and they immediately said that they were having some problems and could sure use my help. So, I went back to the OR and scrubbed in – no one worried about malpractice insurance or credentialing me for privileges on their medical staff, or any of that stuff. Instinctively, they and I were just interested in just getting the patient taken care of, and that's what we did. The patient was a teenage girl and they were operating on her for appendicitis, but the appendix was not in its usual location and they couldn't find it. Fortunately that was part of my surgical training, to learn about the malrotation of the colon. The appendix is attached to the cecum, which is the first part of the right colon, and in the fetal stages, rotation of the colon occurs such that the appendix and cecum are normally located in the right lower quadrant of the abdomen. But if there is incomplete or malrotation of the colon, it can be located in any number of different anatomic locations. So, after assessing the situation, I enlarged her incision to give me more access to the abdomen, located and removed the inflamed appendix, and she subsequently did well. This was my second most memorable appendectomy and the beginning of many years of a long lasting professional relationship with my colleagues in Levelland.

Early Pioneers

Also, I started to receive a lot of referrals from Dr. J.W. Chatwell of Amherst, Texas. He was also from Sudan, a year ahead of me, and practiced in Amherst and later on in Littlefield. From Littlefield I also developed referrals from Dr. Clifford Payne, Dr. Ralph Maurer and Dr. Jack Still. Dr. Clarise Phillips was another older Levelland physician who was an early supporter of mine as well. Dr. Phillips was an Army General during WWII and had headquarters for a period of time at the Hotel Deauville on the Normandy coast. He had told me before I was stationed in Paris that the manager of that hotel was still there and that I should visit him sometime if I had the opportunity. So, at the first opportunity I made a trip up to Deauville to visit that historic place.

This was the first of many trips I made to the Normandy beaches to view the site of the Allied invasion onto French soil on June 6, 1944, to begin the liberation of the French from German occupation.

The two big names in surgery in Lubbock when I arrived to start my practice at Methodist Hospital were "B&R," Drs. Al Bronwell and Randy Rutledge. They and I became good friends over the years, but early on as I was getting my practice started, I envied them because they consistently had five or six operations scheduled every day and were really quality surgeons whom everyone respected. Both were board trained and certified by the American College of Surgeons. Two other doctors whom I enjoyed working with and respected were Dr. "Babe" English and Dr. Ewell Hunt, who were old-timers in Lubbock and had a longstanding partnership. Both were family practitioners, but doing some surgery in Lubbock at the old West Texas Hospital downtown. They both had sons who later were to become board certified surgeons.

I first started practice with Dr. Jack Selby, a highly trained general and thoracic surgeon. Jack was the first thoracic surgeon in all of West Texas. He was trained in the East in Boston and had that rugged New England look and bore a striking resemblance to the Kennedy clan, especially Ted Kennedy. He was an extremely versatile surgeon. Not only did he do general and lung surgery, but he also did the first heart surgery in West Texas in the 1950s. The heart/lung machine had not been perfected at that time and the heart surgery he did, which I helped him on, was mainly on the heart valves. Rheumatic fever back in those days resulted sometimes in the formation of scar tissue on the heart valves, and the operation to repair the scarred valves was done with the heart beating, consisting of making an opening in the upper chamber of the heart, the auricle, and then passing an instrument or a finger with an attachment on the finger, opening up the scarred valve which would allow the valve to function normally. This was quite a "hairy" operation in those days, but done well by Dr. Selby.

I initially made $10,000 my first year in Lubbock, but considerably more than the $25 a month Dr. DeBakey paid me as a first-year resident.

Some of the earliest physician pioneers in Lubbock were Dr. M.C. Overton (who is credited with being the first licensed physician in 1901), Dr. J.T. Hutcheson (the first eye, ear, nose and throat specialist) and Dr.

J.T. Krueger (general surgeon). The three of them built a multimillion dollar, 280-bed hospital on 19th Street in 1953, called Lubbock Memorial Hospital. A year later the Northwest Texas Conference of the Methodist Church assumed ownership, renamed it Methodist Hospital and made it an open staff hospital. In my mind, this was one of the major events in Lubbock's medical history. Prior to this, all of the medical facilities in Lubbock were proprietarily owned, with closed medical staffs, but when Methodist became open to any qualified physician, this was a stimulus for many new physicians to come to Lubbock, making it the major medical hub in West Texas. It was certainly one of the main reasons I located in Lubbock.

So, these three early physician pioneers and the Methodist church deserve the credit for creating the platform on which Lubbock has developed into the city with some of the finest facilities and physicians one can find anywhere in the world.

First Office

After I left practice with Dr. Selby I opened my own" little shop" in a medical office building attached to the original Methodist Hospital. It was a small four-room suite – one waiting room, one exam room, one treatment room and one office. Dr. J.T. Krueger had offered me the opportunity to practice in his group, but I preferred to maintain my own independence and autonomy. I felt like I wanted to be my own boss and not have to be accountable to any one else and I wanted to establish my own identity and reputation. I realized that a position with him would offer me immediate security and an easier path perhaps, but in the long run I felt that I would be happier going it alone.

I had an office staff of one person, Loeta Selman. She had no formal training in office practice management or nursing, but was a jack of all trades. She was my receptionist, nurse, insurance clerk, business manager and accountant.

One day shortly after I opened my office, I was doing some minor surgery in the treatment room removing, under local anesthesia, a lesion from the back of the leg of a patient who was lying prone with the face down. The patient inadvertently raised her legs up knocking my scalpel off of the instrument tray, and it was propelled directly into my thigh like a dagger, sticking into my leg and I couldn't shake it loose. It immediately started bleeding through my pants, down my leg, into my shoe and onto the floor. I had on sterile gloves and hadn't completed the surgery on the patient yet, and surely didn't want her to know what had happened. So, I made enough racket that Loeta came into the room and about fainted when she saw what had happened. I motioned to her with my head to remove the scalpel from my thigh, and I finished sewing up the patient and then left the room without her ever knowing what had happened. I had dread fear that if she had known what had happened the rumor would get out that I had stuck myself with my own scalpel, and it certainly would not be the type of recommendation I would want just getting my practice started.

Loeta was a great lady, fiercely loyal to me, but later on developed breast cancer and ultimately succumbed to that disease. I will always remember her and be grateful to her for helping me get started, and for her devotion to me.

Disillusioned

One of the first things I wanted to do when I returned to Lubbock was look up my old friend, Wayne Bowles with whom I played basketball at Texas Tech as a freshman. Wayne had been a Pre-Med student, like myself. After the first year at Texas Tech, I knew I was not capable of continuing to try to play basketball and at the same time do well in my Pre-Med classes, many of which had all afternoon laboratory work as well as the one-hour classroom lecture. So, at the end of the year I gave up any aspiration of playing basketball (which I didn't excel at anyway, as Wayne did), but Wayne continued doing both. He was about 6'6" in height, which was a giant at that time, and went on to become an All-Border Conference player (this was before Texas Tech participated in the Southwest and Big 12 Conferences). He continued with his Pre-Med studies while becoming a basketball star. I'm assuming his grades were probably affected by the long hours required for him to become an elite ballplayer, and he didn't get into medical school. So, when I went off to medical school, I had always wondered what happened to Wayne. When I returned to Lubbock I tracked him down in Santa Fe and gave him a call, and he asked me to come up and see him on the weekend.

I was feeling so sorry for him all the while because he didn't get into medical school 12 years earlier.

Well, as it turned out, Wayne had done quite well for himself during that period of time. He owned a motel and a liquor store, and went hunting and fishing all the time, enjoying the good life. And here I was without a dime to my name, deep in debt from residency training, just beginning to start a practice and I felt as though he had already reached the pinnacle of his career.

I have to confess that on the way back from Santa Fe to Lubbock, my feelings and emotions just completely flip-flopped. Now, I was feeling sorry for myself instead of Wayne and wondered if I had made the right decision for myself in going to medical school.

SWAT Team

Over time I developed a large surgical practice, and as the practice grew I kept adding partners. My first was Dr. Jerry Stirman, who had been on the faculty at Southwestern Medical School in Dallas – an extremely brilliant and talented surgeon, who was ambidextrous, operating equally well with either hand. After a few years of this two-man partnership, Dr. Ted Allen, a Lubbock native, joined us. Ted had trained with Dr. DeBakey in Houston and was equally talented, so we had a lot in common. After a period of time, Dr. Teb Thames and Dr. Tim West (whose father was Dirk West, mayor of Lubbock in 1978 and who was an editorial cartoonist and journalist who became famous for his works featuring collegiate mascots of schools in the old Southwest Conference), also Lubbock natives, joined us. Subsequently, Dr. Stirman retired after some health issues, leaving the four of us – Salem, West, Allen and Thames to form the SWAT Team, as we were affectionately called. The nurses actually were the genesis of the SWAT Team name. They took the first letter of each of our last names and made SWAT out of it. We took rotational call at the hospital and they got tired of writing, "consult Dr. Salem, Dr. Allen, Dr. Thames, and Dr. West," and so they condensed it into SWAT, and that's how the SWAT name originated.

As Aaron Latham referred to us in his book, The Ballad of Gussie & Clyde, published in 1997 in a chapter entitled The SWAT Team, "They handled most of the triage cases in and around Lubbock. Plane crashes and train wrecks, automobile accidents and lightning burns, knifings and shootings – they were all their meat. If you need some cutting done right now, then you needed them."

Dr. Beth Nickels, our first and only female partner, attended Mr. Latham's father during his surgical illness. Other partners joined SWAT over the years including Dr. Craig Rhyne, Dr. Mark Pessa, Dr. Sam Campbell, Dr. Charles Bayouth, Dr. Richard Rosen, Dr. Job Buschman, Dr. Sammy Deeb, and most recently Dr. Tom Howe and Dr. Barnard Barragan.

Ruptured Abdominal Aortic Aneurysm

One of the first major vascular cases I had shortly after I arrived turned out to be one of the most challenging. I had just recently had the hospital order and received the specialized grafts, instruments and suture material to do major vascular surgery when I received this call in the middle of the night from a prominent family practitioner, Dr. Sam Dunn, who worked primarily at a downtown hospital, West Texas Hospital. He said, "I hear you are new in town but know how to do this blood vessel surgery, and I think this patient has one of those abdominal aneurysms that may have ruptured, and can you come and take care of him?" Ruptured aneurysms are one of the true surgical emergencies. Life or death hinges on prompt surgical intervention. So I went immediately to see the patient and transferred him back to Methodist Hospital where I was doing most of my surgery. With an assistant and OR crew helping me, none of whom had ever seen this type of surgery nor had ever been in-serviced on this procedure, I began the surgical procedure with much anxiety and trepidation.

This particular aneurysm was unlike any I had ever seen before. Most abdominal aortic aneurysms rupture posteriorly into the area of the back called the retroperitoneum, but this one had ruptured into the large vein (vena cava) that runs adjacent to the aorta on the right side. This had created a massive arterio-venous fistula--an abnormal connection between the artery and the vein--and resulted in the shunting of large volumes of blood into the vena cava which then resulted in overloading of the right heart. In all of my years of operating on abdominal vascular cases in Houston, I had never seen this particular entity and therefore was not entirely sure how to manage it. But following general vascular surgical principles, I was able to disconnect the fistula, repair the hole in the vena cava and replace the aneurysm with a synthetic aortic graft.

He recovered from this rather horrendous operation without any major complications, lived a normal lifespan, and twenty years later I would operate on him again to remove his gallbladder and repair a diaphragmatic hernia.

So, my career got off to a quick jump start with this case, and I always had an abundance of surgical patients to operate on – hence the addition of multiple partners over the years.

Bobby Layne – Football Legend
Another interesting case I had was on a famous football player who had married the daughter of one of Lubbock's earliest and most renowned physicians, Dr. J.T. Krueger. Bobby Layne was an All-American quarterback for the University of Texas and later an All-Pro for the Detroit Lions, and had married Dr. Krueger's daughter, Carol Ann. A few years after he retired from football he began to have bleeding episodes from his esophagus secondary to scarring in his liver.

He had been to several prominent hospitals in the country for medical treatment, but was not felt to be a surgical candidate due to his poor liver function. He was visiting in Lubbock one weekend and began to have a major bleeding episode, which could not be controlled by all conservative medical measures. I was awakened about 5 a.m. by one of my partners, Ted Allen, and he said, "Bob, are you awake?" I said, "Well, yes, Ted, I am now, what do you need?" He said, "Well, you need to come to the OR right away. We've been working all night trying to get Bobby Layne's bleeding stopped and can't seem to stem the tide, and he will bleed to death shortly if we don't do something. The family wants you to try and do a portacaval shunt on him. He's on the OR table now and we are waiting for you to get here."

Well, being awakened like this for a problem of this magnitude on a high-profile person is quite a heavy load. This type of surgical procedure shunts the blood from the liver and esophageal (visceral) area to the systemic venous system circulation thereby reducing the pressure in the esophageal veins, allowing the bleeding to stop on its own. Under these circumstances it carries a very high mortality rate.

This particular operation was certainly one of the most difficult for any surgeon to perform. Because of the tremendous back pressure built up, there is always a huge amount of bleeding and it is always a race against time—can you get the shunt done and lower the pressure before the patient bleeds to death.

Today this problem can be alleviated by the interventional radiologist with a procedure called TIPS in which a shunt is placed in the liver through a catheter in a minimally invasive operation that accomplishes the same thing without major surgical intervention. But this technique was not available then.

So, after talking with the family, they wished for me to proceed. With Ted helping me and after an arduous several-hour operation, we were able to successfully perform the surgery, lower the pressure and stop the hemorrhaging. He received multiple units of blood during the operation and was critically ill for several days but did manage to survive the immediate post operative period.

Bobby lived for a few weeks following surgery, but had progressive liver and renal failure, and finally succumbed. I indicated to the family later that I had never known anyone to endure the ravages of illness with the fortitude and sheer guts that Bobby had.

I attended his wake in Lubbock at which many of his old NFL football buddies spoke and reminisced about his NFL football career, and it was quite a bash. Later on, renowned author Bob St. John would chronicle the life of Bobby Layne in a book entitled "The Heart of a Lion," which recounts his life's story and last days of his life in Lubbock, Texas.

Survival--The Mark Scioli Saga

This probably has been the most incredible and miraculous story of my entire surgical career. It has to do with an accidental gunshot wound sustained by a high school student at the time—Mark Scioli.

Shortly after midnight one day in June, 1973, as I was completing an already extremely long day, I received an urgent telephone call from another surgeon, Dr. Ray Mann, who practiced at a smaller hospital in Lubbock. He informed me that he had just seen this teenaged boy in his small emergency room who had been accidentally shot in the abdomen with a rifle by a friend of his, another teenager, while they were out hunting coyotes at night. He said that the young man was in profound shock and appeared to be bleeding from injuries sustained in the abdomen. He said he did not feel he could manage this serious of an injury at his hospital and asked if I could take care of him at Methodist Hospital, which was the major trauma hospital at the time.

He also told me that the patient didn't look very good and he wasn't even sure if he would survive the ambulance ride over to Methodist (some 10-15 minutes). I told him that I would accept the patient and instructed him to start IV fluids and get him in an ambulance to Methodist Hospital as soon as possible. Immediately after the telephone conversation with Dr. Mann, I notified the operating room to prepare for an emergency gunshot wound of the abdomen. I met the patient in the emergency room and prepared him for immediate surgery. He remained in deep shock as we began restoration of his blood volume with IV fluids and transfusions.

I informed the family that I would do everything possible to save his life, but that there are some cases where the shock has gone on for such a long time that it becomes irreversible, resulting in loss of all organ functions—and inevitable death. I feared that we were approaching that critical time and that his chances for survival were not real good.

At surgery, he was found to have sustained massive intra abdominal injuries to multiple organs and major blood vessels. I was, however, able to repair everything and stop the hemorrhaging. Gradually, thereafter, his blood pressure slowly, but steadily, began to rise and return to normal where it stabilized.

The bullet had also injured his spinal cord resulting in a permanent injury to some nerves going to his leg, but otherwise, over the next few days, he seemed to be recovering from his other injuries satisfactorily. When it appeared we were about "out of the woods," he developed an abscess in the abdomen with some adhesions obstructing his intestines, requiring a second operation. So with considerable consternation, I decided I needed to return him to surgery, realizing that on the first trip to the O.R. we were most fortunate to have had a good outcome.

Shortly after the induction of the anesthetic agents, the patient sustained a completely unsuspected full cardiac arrest that was totally inexplicable and the most dreaded of all experiences in the O.R. I immediately began closed cardiac massage and within a matter of a very few minutes, his cardiac function returned to normal. I then had to make a decision—do we abort the planned surgery—or do we go on with it? After consultation with the cardiologist and the anesthesiologist, we made the decision to go forward with the operation. We were able to deal surgically with the abscess and adhesions satisfactorily and the remainder of the operation progressed without further incidents. After this second operation, his progress was quite good and it appeared that he would be able to be discharged from the hospital soon and continue the rehab on his leg.

Then suddenly another serious complication arose—he began to have massive bleeding from a stress ulcer of his stomach. All attempts at conservative management to stop the bleeding were unsuccessful and I had no alternative but to return him to the O.R. for yet another operation—his third. He had had a complete cardiac and anesthetic workup and nothing was identified at this point that might have triggered his prior cardiac arrest, but nonetheless, I asked the cardiologist to be in the O.R. with me during this third operation from the very beginning.

He obliged us and was at the head of the table by the anesthesiologist as the operation began. To my chagrin and dismay, the patient sustained another cardiac arrest just before the incision was made and then all of our attention was directed at trying to restore cardiac function. I immediately began closed cardiac massage, as I had done previously, while the anesthesiologist administered 100% oxygen and the cardiologist delivered appropriate cardiac medications intravenously.

This time, however, cardiac function did not resume as on the prior occasion—the heart remained in complete standstill—no beat—no movement—totally without any contractions. I thought to myself, "surely electrical stimulation will start up the heart," so I immediately shocked the heart with the paddles and anxiously watched the EKG----no heartbeat. Shocked the heart a second time----still no beats. And then a third time----and to my dismay…still nothing. So when this didn't work, I resumed cardiac compression for another 20 minutes or so. Finally the cardiologist advised me that I should probably discontinue my efforts. He felt like the heartbeat was not likely to return after this period of time and even if it did, the patient would very likely have severely impaired brain function.

I refused to accept this suggestion at this point because we know that children tolerate cerebral anoxia (decreased circulation and oxygenation of the brain) better than adults and that is why the airline attendants recommend that if the cabin of the airplane loses pressurization and the oxygen masks drop down, that you are advised to first put the mask on the adult's face and then secondarily apply the mask to the child's face.

While my patient was not a child, but rather a young adult, I felt he might respond more like a child rather than a mature adult, with regard to deprivation of the brain with circulation and oxygenation. So I told the cardiologist that I would continue cardiac massage for another five minutes and if cardiac function did not resume by then, I would quit.

Well, shortly after that and by the grace of God, his cardiac beat suddenly returned and to the amazement of all, the EKG once again did not reveal any obvious significant damage to the heart. Everyone was rejoicing over the events as they unfolded, but then the reality of the moment set in. We were faced once again with an extremely difficult choice and dilemma. Should we abort the operation in view of this sustained period of cardiac arrest or do we proceed now with an operation to stop the bleeding from the stress ulcer? I was utterly exhausted and devastated by the events by this time, but, as before, at the second operation, felt that his only chance for survival was to push on with the surgery, even under these horrific circumstances, which is what we did. Fortunately, and gratefully, the surgery was successful, the bleeding controlled, and there were no further cardiac events. His recovery thereafter was uneventful and he was finally discharged from the hospital, but requiring continued rehabilitation for his nerve and leg impairments.

One might presume that this was the end of the story, but we're only halfway there. This young man graduated from high school the next year and ultimately went on to medical school at Texas Tech graduating as Mark Scioli, M.D. in 1982 and as the recipient of the Gold Headed Cane Award, the school's most prestigious award given to that person who best exemplifies and embodies the principals and ideals to become a great physician.

Mark decided to specialize in Orthopedic surgery and during his residency came back to see me one day, having developed a hernia in his abdominal incision from his three previous abdominal operations. He asked me if I would repair his hernia, whereupon I reminded him with, "Mark, do you recall that you have already had three close calls with death from your prior accident and surgeries? So why don't we consider just getting you an abdominal support and not run the risk of yet another operation, still not knowing for sure what caused some of your difficulties?" But he was rather adamant about getting this fixed as he felt it would hinder him in his profession as an orthopedic surgeon because this particular specialty demands a large amount of physical strength and use of the arms and abdominal musculature in the performance of orthopedic procedures. I don't blame him for pushing on this and probably would have done the same had I been in his shoes.

So back for a fourth procedure we go. By now there was some additional sophisticated testing available that we did on various medications that might have been implicated in his prior cardiac difficulties and we did most of these prior to returning him to the O.R. On induction of the anesthetic for this fourth surgery, his heart rate began to slow severely, but he did not go into full cardiac arrest, so I immediately aborted the procedure, as this was purely an elective operation. After additional testing we finally discovered what we thought might be the culprit. He had been having, we thought, an idiosyncratic allergic reaction to one of the drugs commonly used in putting a patient to sleep for a surgical procedure, which accounted, we felt, for his heart to stop beating. We felt reasonably confident we had now identified the problem and returned him again for the fifth time using entirely different anesthetic protocols. This last time around was completely uneventful. No problem with the anesthesia or heart and surgical repair of his abdominal hernia and post operative course was uncomplicated.

This remarkable story of survival has been embedded in my psyche for many years now and to have witnessed the sheer will and determination of this young man through his early years in dealing with his multiple operations and disabilities of his leg and nerve injuries has been an illuminating experience for me and I'm sure for all who have known him. And in spite of all the adversities to which he has been subjected, he has developed into one of Lubbock's most respected and renowned orthopedic surgeons.

It has truly been an inspirational story!

Tale of Two Sheriffs

Once I had operated on at the same time by coincidence, the Sheriffs of Lamb County (in which Sudan is located) and neighboring Bailey County. One day as I was making evening ward rounds, they were both in the same room cajoling with each other and when I entered the room they laughingly said that they had been talking respectfully, but critically, about my dad. I asked them what that was all about, and they said that they go to all of this effort and time and energy to capture all of these people who commit burglaries, assault and the like, put them in jail to prosecute them, and then in comes my dad, feeling that there is good in every human being and bails them out, and tries personally to rehabilitate them. Well, that was my dad. I don't know what his success rate was, but I guess if you save one person from a jail sentence or worse it may be worth the effort. In his mind, it was.

The Tornado (That I Almost Slept Through)

Two-term popular Mayor of Lubbock, W.D. "Dub" Rogers, my future father-in-law (although I didn't know it at the time) barely escaped having the responsibility of leading Lubbock through its most catastrophic event in history. Dub was one of the pioneers of the television industry. He founded the first television station in Lubbock in 1952, KDUB TV, which was the first TV station in the world to open in a medium-sized market as Lubbock was. He was elected mayor in 1966 as a write- in candidate and then was re-elected for a second term in 1968. Because of his popularity, he was encouraged by many to run for a third term in 1970, but declined to do so. Just a few weeks after his second term ended, devastation struck Lubbock.

On the evening of May 11, 1970, I knew we had had a bad storm – the TV station had gone out and the radio was reporting high winds and storm damage, but no specific tornado. I wasn't on call that night, but decided to call the emergency room at Methodist Hospital to be sure

I wasn't needed for any emergencies. The nurse said, "Oh, we're okay – just a few minor emergencies." So, I told her to call me if she needed any additional help and went on to bed thinking everything was just fine. About 1 a.m. I was awakened by a telephone ring. It was a doctor from Littlefield, Texas, about 30 miles from Lubbock, and he said, "Bob, I hate to bother you with all that's going on in Lubbock tonight, but I've got this patient who is hemorrhaging from an ulcer and I can't get it stopped, and I think she will need surgery." I said, "Oh, we've just got a few minor injuries, send your patient on over and I'll take care of her." I'm sure he thought I must have been bonkers after I learned the extent later of the massive number of casualties and property destruction – 26 dead, 500 injured and millions of dollars in property destruction.

I called the nurse in the ER again to tell her my patient would be arriving shortly from Littlefield with a bleeding ulcer, she said, "Where in the hell have you been? The ER is full of patients injured from a massive tornado. They've spilled over into all of the hallways, and all operating rooms are going with emergency operations and we have had several fatalities." I responded back, "Well, why in the hell didn't you call me back when all this started coming in?" She said that it all happened so quickly and the impact was so overwhelming that she simply forgot to call. The doctors on call were, of course, immediately called and responded, and were initiating treatment for the massive number of injuries.

Methodist Hospital at the time was the only major hospital in the city to handle a major trauma of this type. This was before the medical school and the university hospital were built, so Methodist bore the full brunt of this devastating and massive mass casualty event. At the time we had 280 beds and 12 operating rooms.

After I talked to the nurse in the ER, I immediately went to the hospital. On the way I saw tell-tale signs of a massive destructive force – tree limbs in the streets, houses destroyed, telephone lines down, debris everywhere. When I arrived at the hospital I could not believe what I saw. It reminded me of the mass casualties I dealt with in the two major airline crashes while I was a doctor with the USAF at Orly Airfield in Paris, France, that I alluded to earlier in Chapter 5. All ER rooms were filled, patients were on litters and lined up and down in all adjacent hallways. Scores of others with minor injuries were seated in available chairs all over the place.

I rapidly got on my scrubs and sprang into action along with the other surgeons. Trauma surgery is initially a matter of triage. You immediately assess and determine those patients who need lifesaving surgery right away and deal with those first. Then those whose condition is not as critical are stabilized, given supportive treatment and surgery done later on.

So, that was the process and protocol. I was in the operating room for the rest of the night and all day the next day operating on those patients who needed emergency surgery, and then later for those that were not as critical. The patient from Littlefield arrived in the midst of all this chaos. I saw her in the ER and determined that she could be stabilized, treated with blood transfusions and medications, but would probably need surgery for definitive treatment later, but felt I could defer her for the moment.

After all of the victims were taken care of, I then directed my attention to my bleeding ulcer patient. I determined that she was continuing to bleed, so I took her to surgery late in the afternoon of the day following the tornado and removed a portion of her stomach containing the bleeding ulcer. By this time I had operated for over 24 hours straight. Fortunately, she did well postoperatively, as did all of the patients we operated upon for injuries resulting from the tornado.

This was the third major disaster that I had dealt with in my surgical career including the two major airline crashes in France and I hoped the last. We continue to this day to have "disaster drills" which I think are appropriate and necessary, and all of the planning and mock drills are helpful, but yet when the real deal happens and you're right in the middle of the heat of the battle, you draw on what you've learned and practiced, but also you perform intuitively on instinct.

Yes, 26 lives were lost on that fateful night in Lubbock, Texas, but scores more were saved by the prompt and decisive action of the dedicated doctors, nurses, support staff, volunteers and administrative staff of the hospital, as well as tremendous support from the city – fire and police departments, and city officials in particular.

The lessons learned from that disaster are many, but the two major obstacles that we experienced were two in number - #1 communications and #2 water supply.

Telephone lines were down and communication with all parties was difficult. Water supplies were shut off and we had to bring in bottled water to supply our water needs in the OR and throughout the hospital.

All in all though, the Lubbock community responded to this horrible event in a remarkable manner, was the model for the management of a major tornadic event, and the experience gained will bode well for the people of this area in the future, should another disaster strike late in an evening one day.

I will always be grateful to the doctor who called me in the middle of the night to care for his patient; otherwise, I might have slept through the night and missed the opportunity to render aid to those for whom I spent years in training to provide.

Heart Surgery Development in West Texas

One of the things I am most proud of in my career is in helping to bring cardiac surgery to the people of West Texas and Eastern New Mexico. Dr. Sam King began to do heart catherizations at Methodist Hospital, followed by Dr. Joe Arrington and others. As they saw patients who might need a coronary artery bypass procedure, they were having to send their patients out of the city for surgery. So, they came to me knowing I had trained at one of the most notable programs in the world with Dr. DeBakey in Houston, and asked if I might know or help recruit someone to come to Lubbock to start up an Open Heart Surgical Program. The heart/lung machine had become perfected by this time and that allowed these procedures to be done safely.

I immediately thought of one of my junior residents at the time I was in training – Dr. Don Bricker. Although I hadn't had any contact with him since I had finished my training, I remembered him as a bright, hard-working resident who had come down from Cornell in New York to Houston to learn how to do heart and vascular surgery. Don was from Wyoming originally and I thought he might adapt to the geography and culture of West Texas, and would not be daunted by the enormous challenge of starting up a heart surgical program from scratch in a midsize West Texas city.

So, I called Don up and set the stage for him, emphasizing what a unique opportunity this would be – the first program of its kind in the entire area in this size city. Don had a comfortable and highly responsible and secure job in Houston working with Dr. DeBakey and Dr. Cooley, as Chief Surgeon at Ben Taub Hospital. But he agreed to come out for a look, and after a couple of visits made the huge decision to move to Lubbock and accept the challenge.

So, he joined me and Dr. Stirman in our practice, and we lent support to him to get this program off the ground successfully. There was significant resistance from some of the medical staff, and even administration and board members. Some of them thought that surgery of this type should never be done in a relatively small hospital and city such as Lubbock. But Don and I and others felt differently. It is a tremendous emotional and financial sacrifice for families and patients to have to be sent out of town, away from the personal support of their environment and friends and families. So, we wanted to be able to provide the people of this area with the expertise and comfort of having this type of surgical treatment done at home.

Furthermore, the naysayers and doubters didn't have a clue as to the grit and determination and confidence of DeBakey-trained surgeons, Bricker and Salem. DeBakey actually was supportive of his residents going out over the world to practice the art of surgery he had taught them, even in West Texas.

Needless to say, there was a lot riding on that first operation. Not only our own personal reputations, but the reputation of the hospital and the whole future of cardiovascular surgery in West Texas hinged on how successful we were at the outset.

So, we had many dry runs, many hours of education for all of the OR staff, and for everyone associated with that program. Then that eventful day finally arrived, November 27, 1970. Dr. Bricker successfully operated on the first patient in West Texas using a heart/ lung machine (administered so capably by his current wife, Sammie Lou) and I assisted him in the procedure. For several months thereafter Don would sleep by the patient's side for several days to be sure that everything went well, and until the SICU staff was comfortable in managing the patients. Occasionally I would relieve him.

From that beginning, we built the third largest heart surgical program in the state – 1,200 open heart surgical cases per year, with the addition of other cardiovascular surgeons to our medical staff. The doubters and the naysayers rapidly faded into oblivion and everyone jumped on the bandwagon, heaping praise and congratulations to all involved.

In 2001 we expanded our successful Adult Heart Surgical Program to include children, and I recruited Dr. Jim Harrell, who had had a highly successful tenure at Arkansas Children's Hospital in Little Rock doing pediatric heart surgery as well as cardiac transplant surgery. He, like Don, could have pursued a less challenging course and gone to an already established program, but like Don also, he was stimulated and invigorated by the challenge of starting up a formal Children's Heart Surgical Program in West Texas.

This successful program under Dr. Harrell's leadership, assisted by his wife Marty, who is a Pediatric Cardiac nurse, has continued to grow year by year and is providing children and their parents and families the comfort of having the most complex of congenital heart problems managed here at home.

Texas Tech University Medical School
Another of my pleasant memories of practice and living in Lubbock has been with my relationship and activity with the Texas Tech Medical School. I was involved with the school from the very early planning days, feeling that if a new medical school were to come to West Texas that it should be in Lubbock, affiliated with Texas Tech.

Bill Parsley, longtime good friend, attorney, Texas House Representative, and Vice President for Development at Texas Tech, as he was developing plans for the political alignments to successfully get a bill passed for a Texas Tech Medical School, asked me to accompany him on trips to Austin. At the time I was Chief of Staff of Methodist Hospital and President of the Lubbock/Crosby/Garza County Medical Society, and he wanted me along as his medical sounding board and resource.

We met several times at the bar of the 40 Acres Club in Austin, which used to be a common political hangout, and I had the impression that many sensitive decisions were made in the bar rather than in the halls of Congress.

Bill would meet with Frank Erwin, the Chairman of the Board of

Regents of the University of Texas, and many people told me that he was one of the most powerful men in Texas, as much, or more so than the governor. So, he and Bill would discuss medical school developments – Texas Tech wanted one and the University of Texas also wanted another one in Houston. The original bill to create one at Texas Tech earlier, which had been spearheaded through the House of Representatives by Delwin Jones and through the Senate by my old Sudan buddy, "Doc" Blanchard, had been vetoed by Governor John Connally. So, this time around we wanted to garner support from the University of Texas System for our school so it could become a reality and not be vetoed again. After about 1 o'clock in the morning and a couple of drinks I would leave Bill and Frank still talking and negotiating, and I would retire, and their discussions went on for some time thereafter.

To my way of thinking, Bill Parsley never got the credit or notoriety that I think he should have received for his major contributions in the development of the medical school through his behind-the-scenes negotiations.

So, after several discussions at the 40 Acres Club and I'm sure many others with a lot of folks in many other places, the bill creating the medical school for Texas Tech was finally passed in 1969. Fortuitously, Preston Smith, a Lubbock native, had been elected Governor of Texas in 1968, so when the bill came up for the second time for a Governor's signature, he had no problem signing it. There were provisions in the bill to provide the participation by facilities in Amarillo, El Paso and Midland-Odessa in the educational process through formal affiliation agreements.

A number of years later, Bill had been in Austin and had had to have urgent surgery for an abdominal aortic aneurysm. I had not been aware of this until in the middle of the night after he returned to Lubbock, his wife, Alice, called me extremely apprehensive. She said that she felt something terrible was going on with both of Bill's legs. She told me about the surgery in Austin and said that on return to Lubbock a few hours earlier, that suddenly his legs had become painful and had turned a mottled blue in color. I immediately suspected that he had had a sudden occlusion of the blood supply to both legs, probably from some blood clot in the graft or other arteriosclerotic debris in his aortic graft.

84

When one does surgery for an abdominal aortic aneurysm, one removes the aneurysm and replaces that segment of the aorta (the main artery) in the abdomen with a synthetic Dacron graft. If the aneurysm is lower down, it may involve the bifurcation of the aorta where it divides into a right and a left branch going down into each leg, in which case the replacement is made with a bifurcated graft much like an inverted Y.

I told Alice to immediately take Bill to the ER and I would meet her there. When I saw him I could tell that he had no blood flow to either leg and if I was not able to restore circulation, he was in jeopardy of losing both legs, and time was critical. So, I immediately took him to the operating room and called Don Bricker to help me, as I wanted to get blood flow to both legs as soon as possible, and another experienced surgeon in dealing with this type of emergency would facilitate a more immediate resolution.

After a couple of hours we restored circulation to both legs. He developed normal pulses in both legs and feet, and the mottled blue discoloration returned to a healthy pink. Whew – another close call, but a good result.

As plans to open the medical school progressed, a decision was made to enroll a third-year class along with a freshman class. I was asked by Dean John Buesseler, the first Dean of the medical school, if I would head up the Department of Surgery, as they had not had time to recruit a full-time faculty for the clinical services, such as surgery, pediatrics, OB/Gyn, etc. I was reluctant to do this. First of all, I had a full-time private surgical practice that was all-consuming, and although I had an interest in academia, I really didn't have a background in this and felt inadequate. But wanting to help anyway I could to see the school succeed, I finally agreed to take on the challenge. What I thought initially would be a three to six-month job turned into a three-year task before we were able to recruit Dr. Francis Jackson to be the full-time professor and Chairman of the Department of Surgery. I initially gave most of the lectures in surgery to the third-year class, and about the only time I could do this was at 7 a.m. Saturday. After a period of time, the students went to the Dean complaining about me and the Saturday morning lectures. The Dean called me over and said, "Bob, the students have come to me and complained that you were too demanding of them by having your surgery lectures at 7 a.m. on Saturdays, and furthermore, they want to have every other Saturday off." You have to understand that I was donating my time for this help I was giving. For three years I received not a dime for the service I was rendering (this was my way of offering additional support to the school), and for the audacity of the students to complain to the Dean was absolutely insulting and disheartening to me. After I came down off the ceiling and thought about it for a few minutes, I responded back to the Dean with, "You know Dean, the students are right, 7 a.m. Saturday morning is a bad time for surgery lectures. You tell them from now on, starting next Saturday, the lectures will begin at 6:30 a.m. and I'm going to call roll and I expect 100% attendance and tell them further that the final exam in surgery is going to be over nothing but my lectures, so if they aren't there I don't know how in the hell they're going to pass surgery and become doctors." Furthermore, I said, "If you don't support me on this, then I'll tender my resignation right now."

Well, I guess I had the Dean over the barrel to a degree. In any event, he agreed and took my message back to the students and, to their credit, they complied with my dicta and I never heard another word about Saturday morning surgical lectures.

The medical school, although still in its infancy, compared to other schools in the country, continues to thrive and be an increasingly focal point in the medical community in Lubbock, supplying Lubbock and West Texas with many much-needed and sought-after physicians.

On the 25th anniversary of the school, in 1997, those of us who were here at the beginning were asked to recall the early beginnings of the various departments. The following is my account of the development of the Department of Surgery.

"Having grown up in a rural West Texas town that never had a physician and as a graduate of Texas Tech University, I was enthralled with the possibility that my alma mater might become the site of a new medical school.

The location of the medical school was a hotly contested political football, and early on it appeared that Amarillo had the edge. In the end, however, Lubbock's political clout and common sense prevailed, and a medical school was created for West Texas, to be located in Lubbock and with the mission to develop doctors for the underserved population of West Texas with an emphasis on primary care physicians.

In the late '60s and '70s, I served as president of the Lubbock-

86

Crosby-Garza County Medical Society and chief of the medical staff of Methodist Hospital. Like most of the practicing physicians in Lubbock, I was supportive of and actively engaged in many efforts and activities to see the school located in Lubbock.

Nearing time for the school to open, the faculty for the basic science courses of the first two years was pretty well set, but the clinical faculty for the courses of the third and fourth years was lacking. At this point, the practicing physicians in town followed up on the earlier commitment and pledge for support of the medical school – 77 private physicians were approved for, and accepted appointments to, the clinical faculty to shoulder the main teaching responsibilities of the third- and fourth-year students. It was at this point that Dr. John Buesseler, the first dean of the medical school, asked if I would assume the first chair of the Department of Surgery. I agreed to do this on an interim basis, while maintaining my own surgical practice, until a permanent full-time chairman was secured. I was able to do this with the help and cooperation of the other general surgeons in the community.

I immediately made trips to Dallas and Houston to consult with colleagues in the departments of surgery at Southwestern Medical School and Baylor University College of Medicine, respectively. From them I gained insight as to how to establish a surgery department in a new medical school. At this point, there was no medical school building and no county hospital – just a lot of blueprints, and hopes and dreams for the future. Methodist Hospital was designated and agreed to accept the role as interim teaching hospital for the School of Medicine, which was initially housed in Thompson Hall. There were issues of students' access to Methodist Hospital and its private patients, related to affiliation agreements, medical-legal issues, confidentiality concerns, etc.

I set up a curriculum that included a lecture series given by virtually all of the surgeons in Lubbock, who freely gave of their time. Clinical rotations with the general surgeons at Methodist were established so that the students rotated in the operating room with different surgeons. In my mind, this was one of the strongest parts of the surgical rotation, as the students got one-on-one tutorial instruction from board-certified, experienced surgeons and, from a practical perspective, literally functioned as interns in the operating room – unheard of for a third-year medical student.

When I accepted this position, I anticipated that this would be a three to six month task. It took three years, however, before we secured the services of surgeon Dr. Frances C. Jackson, who succeeded me as chairman of the Department of Surgery and who was perfect for the job. While my strong suit was in the clinical area, Dr. Jackson provided much-needed expertise in administrative and organizational skills and added the obvious academic flavor to the department, which it desperately needed.

I continued to work closely with Dr. Jackson as the department matured and developed in experience, and we subsequently established a general surgical residency program. I also had assistance in the first few years from another West Texan, Lubbock native Dr. Maurice Hood, a thoracic surgeon from Austin, who gave up his private practice to assume chairmanship of the Division of Thoracic Surgery. Dr. Jackson and subsequent surgical departmental chairmen, Drs. Peter Canizaro and Tom Shires, brought national recognition and stature to the medical school and to the department of surgery in particular. At the graduation of the first full senior class in June 1975, I was honored by the class by being asked to administer to them the Declaration of Geneva. Alton Ochsner, M.D., Professor Emeritus of Surgery of Tulane University School of Medicine in New Orleans and founder of the famed Ochsner Clinic, delivered the graduation address. As Dr. Ochsner delivered his address to this first medical school graduation class, entitled "Admonitions to the Medical Graduate," I felt an immense sense of pride and exhilaration, much as I had when I received my own MD degree 20 years earlier.

Drawing on some of the lines from Dr. Ochsner's address, 'If a doctor is a true physician, counseling, comforting, and treating with concern and sympathy, he will always be remembered with gratitude. The physician's integrity must be absolute. The good physician must be disciplined.'

Probably the most gratification any professor can receive is for his students to compliment his tutorial style and expertise. I have had the opportunity through the years to associate with numerous former students and residents in all parts of the United Sates. Almost without exception they are most sincerely grateful for the unique opportunity they had to obtain their medical education at Texas Tech and feel that they were provided with superior instruction and experiences that equaled, or surpassed in most cases, that of their peers.

This has made it all worthwhile, and there is no doubt that this institution has elevated the standard of medical care for the people of this area and has fulfilled its mission in providing West Texans with additional primary care physicians. It has been an academic stimulus for me personally, and has challenged all physicians to practice their art at a higher level. TTUHSC and UMC along with the other great medical institutions in this city have established Lubbock as one of the major medical centers in the United States."

The future of Texas Tech University and the Texas Tech Health Sciences Center are quite bright as both are poised to become premier institutions under their current dynamic leadership.

The Chancellor of Texas Tech University, Kent Hance, is a long-time friend who had his roots in the small rural West Texas community of Dimmitt, much like Sudan. He was a professor at Texas Tech for a period of time and my wife, Kay, takes great pride when the Chancellor tells her that she was one of his finest students in the business law class he was teaching when she was a student at Texas Tech. Kent had a distinguished career as an attorney, Texas senator and U.S. congressman before becoming Chancellor of Texas Tech University.

The TTUHSC has had outstanding leadership as well. Dr. John Baldwin was the President until his recent resignation. He has had a distinguished and impressive career both in the surgical world and in medical academia. He is a board certified Thoracic and Cardiovascular surgeon with cardiac/lung transplantation experience and he and I share a common bond with Dr. Michael E. DeBakey. Dr. Baldwin is a former Chairman of the Michael E. DeBakey Department of Surgery at Baylor College of Medicine in Houston. Before assuming the Presidency of the TTUHSC, he served as Dean of Dartmouth Medical School.

The current Dean of the Texas Tech Medical School is Dr. Steven Berk and in the clinical world before he became interested in academia, he was an internal medical specialist, specializing in infectious disease. Dean Berk has been instrumental in fostering better relationships between the fulltime medical school faculty and the community physicians. Under his highly capable leadership, the medical school continues to grow and prosper and Texas Tech has now expanded its scope and horizon with the beginning of a new four-year medical school in El Paso, opening with its first students in the fall of 2009.

As a surgeon, I have always followed with particular interest the progress of the Department of Surgery. For several years now this Department has been vigorously led by its current Chairman, Dr. John Griswold. Dr. Griswold was one of the first surgical residents from the medical school to rotate on my private surgical service at Methodist hospital in the '80s and has established himself as a national figure in the treatment of burns.

Two 1980 Events

Two major events occurred in 1980 that stand out above all others. The first was my marriage to my current wife, Kay. That was a three-for-one package and I acquired two more daughters, Kelly, age 5, and Lauren, age 3. Kelly went on to become a nurse, the only other member of my family who has had any desire to enter the field of healthcare, other than one granddaughter, Erica, who is considering a career in medicine. Kelly works at the Covenant Hospital in Levelland in the OR, and Lauren is a housewife in Fort Worth, Texas, and does a lot of community volunteer work. Each has a boy and a girl.

The other was another exciting and unusual medical emergency case. One day as I finished up my surgery schedule at Methodist Hospital I received this emergent telephone call from a surgeon in the nearby town of Brownfield about forty miles from Lubbock. He was calling from the operating room where he had been doing a gallbladder operation and had begun to experience serious hemorrhaging from an area near the gallbladder. Anxiously he described the situation – he could not identify exactly where the bleeding was coming from and every time he released pressure from the area, the entire operative field was flooded with blood and all he could do was to hold pressure on the area which did temporarily stem the tide of the hemorrhage.

He wanted to know if I could come over immediately and see if I could manage this emergency which was clearly a life-or-death situation. I told him that, yes, I would be there as quickly as possible and told him to do nothing but just hold pressure on the area and try to get the patient hemodynamically stable. I immediately gathered up the necessary vascular instruments and suture material to repair a damaged artery and put them in a bag for travel.

I was driving a Datsun 280 ZX at the time and I called the highway patrol and informed them of the urgent situation and asked if they could give me a police escort to Brownfield. I told them that minutes mattered and I needed to get there as fast as my car could take me. So they immediately provided me with a two-car escort – one in front of me and one behind me. The speedometer on my car had a maximum speed on the panel of 140 mph. So with sirens blaring and lights flashing, we took off and I put the pedal to the floor and got to the maximum speed of 124 mph. We covered that 40 miles in a little over 20 minutes and I was scared to death the whole way. As we approached the city, I didn't even know where the hospital was, but I was met at the city limits by the local sheriff, who escorted me on to the hospital. I immediately scrubbed in and was able to repair the damaged artery successfully and stop the hemorrhage. The patient did well and several weeks later came by my office to thank me personally.

I got such an adrenaline rush from that experience that I thought I would do a repeat. I called the highway patrol again and told them that, "Man, you won't believe this, but I've got another emergency back in Lubbock and I need to get back to Methodist Hospital ASAP." Well they said, "Well, Dr. Salem, you go back as fast as you want to and we won't stop you or ticket you, but we won't be giving you another escort." So I cruised back at a leisurely 100 mph, grateful that we all survived that experience safely, but any fantasies I may have had about being a NASCAR driver were dispelled, or at least significantly dampened, by that trip to Brownfield.

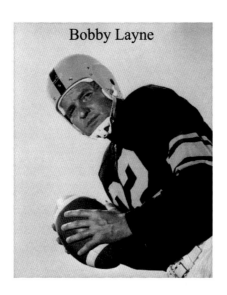
Bobby Layne

LUBBOCK AVALANCHE-JOURNAL

Layne, Former Grid Star, Has Emergency Operation

A-J New Services

Former Detroit Lions star quarterback Bobby Layne of Lubbock was listed in serious condition in Methodist Hospital's surgical Intensive Care Unit after undergoing emergency surgery early Saturday morning.

According to hospital spokesman Doug Hodel, Layne was admitted to the hospital through the emergency room at 2 a.m. with intestinal bleeding. Lubbock surgeon Dr. Robert Salem performed the operation that stopped the bleeding, Hodel said. Layne was reported to be resting comfortably Saturday evening.

Layne's wife Carol told the Associated Press that her husband drove himself the one-half mile to the hospital after he awoke in pain during the night.

Mrs. Layne said her husband was doing well and that all his vital signs were stable and that he had suffered from lower esophagus bleeding, a condition that first appeared a year ago.

Layne returned to Lubbock Wednesday after undergoing treatment at St. Joseph Mercy Hospital in Pontiac, Mich., for a similar problem.

St. Joseph Hospital spokeswoman Madge Lawson told The Avalanche-Journal Layne was released Wednesday. She said she thought he was to return to Texas that day.

Layne had also been in Michigan for a ceremony in which he was to present a professional football Hall of Fame ring to his long-time friend, Doak Walker, in a ceremony during the Detroit-Minnesota game last week.

92

December 22, 1986

Robert J. Salem M.D.
3509 22nd Street
Lubbock, Texas 79410

Dear Bob:

The boys and I read your wonderful letter. It was a great
comfort to all of us. They each asked for a copy which
they now have.

Before now, I knew you mostly through your reputation of
expertise as a surgeon. I was most grateful that you
accepted Bobby as a patient. I was fully aware of the gravity
and difficulty of a porta caval shunt operation. To know Bobby
had the care and personal attention of the finest physicians
anywhere in the world is certainly a great comfort .

I do hope that your true feelings on learning of Bobby's
death was one of regret–not of remorse. Remorse was not
warranteed. You will always have our gratitude and love.

                    Sincerely,

                    Carol Layne

                    Carol Layne

Reprinted from *Texas State Journal of Medicine*, May, 1965, Vol. 61, pp. 394-398

Arteriosclerotic Abdominal Aortic Aneurysm Rupture into the Vena Cava

ROBERT J. SALEM, M.D.

A successfully treated case of arteriosclerotic abdominal aortic aneurysm rupture into the vena cava with resultant large aorto-caval fistula is reported. Included is a comprehensive review of the literature.

SPONTANEOUS RUPTURE of an arteriosclerotic abdominal aortic aneurysm into the inferior vena cava with a resultant aorto-caval fistula is extremely rare. Just how rare is illustrated by the Baylor University surgical group in Houston where in 1,400 cases of surgically treated abdominal aortic aneurysms, only 4 (.28 percent) had ruptured into the vena cava.[1]

This unusual occurrence has been known for many years, but only within the past ten years have successfully treated cases been reported, and these in sparing numbers. Far more common are aorto-caval fistulas complicating penetrating wounds of the abdomen and after lumbar disc surgery. Numerous reports can be found of successful surgical repair of these lesions.

Rupture of an abdominal aortic aneurysm most commonly takes place into the retroperitoneal space and occasionally into the gastrointestinal tract. In a comprehensive review of the English literature over the past ten years, we found only 17 cases of rupture of an abdominal aortic aneurysm into the vena cava. Of this number, 15 were treated surgically, and of the surgically treated cases, 12 had a satisfactory outcome. Our successfully treated case now makes this latter figure 13 (Table 1).

Prior to 1954 when the first successful surgical repair was done, and reported in detail in 1958 by DeBakey and associates,[2] no survivors with this lesion are recorded. Viar and Lombardo reported an earlier case in 1952, but their patient was not operated upon.[3] He lived seven weeks and an autopsy confirmed the findings of an abdominal aortic aneurysm with an aorto-caval fistula.

Of the 12 previously reported successfully treated cases, it is interesting that six (50 percent) have been reported within the past two years. We interpret this finding to indicate several things: first, an increase in incidence of the lesion due to an increasing aged population; second, more alertness as to diagnosis; and third, better surgical technique due to the advancements made in vascular surgery during the past ten years.

A table listing the successfully treated cases is presented with the pertinent data of each, including our own (Table 1). Polak and Skarbek refer to a successfully treated case performed at St. Bartholomew's Hospital in London and this patient is recorded, but the details are not available.[4] Beall and others[1] recorded a successfully treated case by Jaen and Valera which we did not review, but which is also recorded in the list. The similarities of all cases are striking as to the age group, sex, presenting symptoms, and surgical management.

In the unsuccessful surgically treated cases listed in Table 2, it is interesting that three (cases 2, 3, and 4) had cardiac arrests during the early part of the procedure, one due to a massive pulmonary embolus.

Our successfully treated case is presented in detail.

[1]

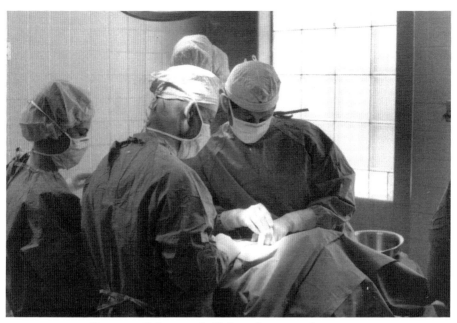

Doctors Stirman & Salem in operating room

ROBERT J. SALEM, M.D., P.A., F.A.C.S.
DEA No. AS 2210110
TED W. ALLEN, M.D., P.A., F.A.C.S.
DEA No. AA 0910732
TEB THAMES, M.D., P.A., F.A.C.S.
DEA No. AT 6501046

3509 22ND STREET   LUBBOCK, TEXAS

TIM L. WEST, M.D., F.A.C.S.
DEA No. AW 9115153
CRAIG D. RHYNE, M.D.
DEA No. AR 1057923
RICHARD A. ROSEN, M.D.
DEA No. BR 0113237

Phone 795-0648

For_____

Address_____ Date _____

SWAT

REFILL_____ TIMES

_____ M.D.   _____ M.D.

DISPENSE AS WRITTEN   PRODUCT SELECTION PERMITTED

Lubbock
Tornado
(1970)

Doctors Bricker
& Salem

To
Bob Salem

You are the
man I always
wanted to be!

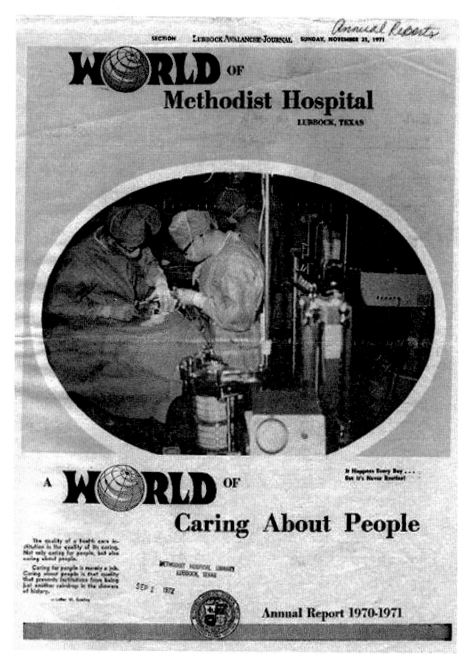

First Open Heart Surgery
Doctors Salem & Bricker (1970)

Doctors Salem, Harrell & Bricker
First Children's Open Heart (2001)

PRESTON SMITH
GOVERNOR OF TEXAS

Medical School Bill Signing (1969)
"Dub Rogers on Governor Smith's Right"

Dr. Buesseler pauses to greet Robert J. Salem, M.D., Clinical Professor and Chairman of the Department of General Surgery.

TTUSM Curriculum Emphasizes Training for Family Practice

Texas Tech University School of Medicine's approach to medical education is unique among medical schools because of the emphasis placed on careers in family practice.

The West Texas region is currently experiencing severe shortages of physicians and serious deficiencies in availability of health care. Because of these problems, TTUSM is oriented to the goal of increasing the number of graduates who will function as primary care physicians.

Medical education at TTUSM stresses family practice and the curriculum is designed to reduce the occurrence of premature specialization on the part of the student. It is felt that early specialization can be harmful to the student because he lacks the necessary base of experience and knowledge to make a wise specialty career choice. The student may decide to concentrate in a particular medical specialty simply because a member of his family, or someone he admires, is such a specialist. Choosing a specialty on this basis is hardly a reliable decision early in the student's educational career. If his interests change later and he becomes interested in a career in family practice, he will find it difficult to adapt because of the narrow focus of his medical school education.

It also is considered that a comprehensive education in the broad spectrum of general medicine is the best preparation a student can acquire for either a career in family practice or in a medical specialty.

The Department of Family Practice plays a vital role in the medical education process at TTUSM. The basic goal of the Department is to emphasize to the students the importance of family practice as a vital and integral part of patient care both in preventive medicine and in whole-family treatment methods, in the context of the family and the community.

The Family Practice Department, in cooperation with other clinical disciplines, will have the responsibility for training medical students and their supportive personnel in the diagnosis and treatment of prevalent illnesses, recognition of rare diseases and in utilization of referral techniques for problem cases. The Family Practice program will demonstrate health maintenance methods through early recognition of change from the norm, through anticipation of such change by recognition of environmental problems and through the natural history of disease and will emphasize the importance of continuity of health care in producing optimal therapeutic results.

Family Practice is a clinical department that functions, not only to teach and train "primary care physicians" but also to

Clinical Faculty Totals 77

Texas Tech University School of Medicine officials have announced the appointments of 59 area physicians to the part-time clinical faculty.

Approved by Dr. Grover E. Murray, President of the University, this brings to 77 the number of physicians appointed to the part-time clinical faculty as of August 31, 1972.

As part-time clinical faculty members, these physicians from Lubbock, Amarillo, and Plainview will teach medical students in the real-world setting of their community hospital and practice environments.

Because the School of Medicine's curriculum is designed to place the student in actual health care settings early in his training, the student will undergo a unique and highly relevant learning experience working with these practicing physicians, Dr. Buesseler said.

Twenty of the new faculty members are in the Department of Internal Medicine, eleven in the Department of Pediatrics, six in the Department of Obstetrics and Gynecology, sixteen in the Department of General Surgery, and six in the Department of Pathology.

serve as a model for organizing the medical health care team. The Department's research is in the search for more effective methods of delivery of medical care; its laboratories are clinical settings such as emergency rooms, ambulatory care centers, nursing homes, physicians' offices and community health care clinics of various types.

The Family Practice curriculum is a blend of classroom study and active participation in the rendering of patient care in clinics. Senior students spend five months in Family Practice Clinic and a four-week Rural Preceptorship program also is part of their training.

Students in the Rural Preceptorship program participate in comprehensive health care delivery in the learning environment of private physicians' offices in rural communities under the supervision and instruction of preceptors appointed by the School of Medicine. The program teaches students how to organize and manage comprehensive health care as well as what a physician does as a member of a community, the community responsibilities he assumes and how he interacts with the community through his practice and through participation in community activities and organizations.

By working with primary care physicians in their community practices, students will be exposed to health care delivery in a real-world situation that can foster an orientation to family practice careers. It is anticipated that many students will choose careers in family medicine and remain to practice in the areas where they received their training.

In addition to the Rural Preceptorship program, the curriculum places students in a variety of clinical settings where they will be able to participate in family health care. In January, 1973, TTUSM and its Department of Family Practice begin operation of an ambulatory patient care facility staffed by the School of Medicine and additional facilities have been made available through affiliation agreements with a number of community hospitals and health care institutions in the TTUSM outreach area.

The Department of Family Practice is currently developing plans for a residency physician training program in Family Practice to be conducted by TTUSM. This program is scheduled to begin in July of 1973. Family Practice residents will participate in primary health care in the environments of the ambulatory facilities at Lubbock, in TTUSM Area Health Education Centers and in rural areas by rotation through the rural practices of selected part-time clinical faculty in the outreach area.

TTUSM's success in meeting the challenge of the health care needs of the medically deprived West Texas area will be largely a product of the focus on the training of highly skilled and knowledgeable family practitioners. The emphasis on family practice, its importance and its rewards for the physician is seen as an important step toward solving the health care needs, not only of the West Texas area, but of the nation as well.

Dean Buesseler & Dr. Salem

TEXAS TECH UNIVERSITY SCHOOL OF MEDICINE

AT LUBBOCK

The 1975 Graduation Convocation

University Center Ballroom

June 8, 1975

Kay & Bob Salem (1980)

8

NEW YORK CITY

Dr. Wayne Isom

Dr. Wayne Isom is one of New York City's leading and most prominent cardiovascular surgeons. He was raised in the little town of Idalou, near Lubbock, much like Sudan where I was raised, and attended Texas Tech University. He went to medical school in Dallas and then did his surgery residency at Parkland Memorial Hospital in Dallas. He then did his cardiothoracic surgery residency with Dr. Frank Spencer at New York University in New York City. He stayed on the faculty at NYU for 12 years and then was recruited to be Chairman at New York Hospital Cornell Medical Center. He has had an illustrious career practicing cardiovascular surgery, operating on many of New York City's most elite and prominent personalities. In spite of his celebrated and distinguished career in the "Big City", he has never forgotten his small town roots and heritage and has always maintained his true West Texas demeanor.

Shortly after September 11, 2001, I went to New York City along with my good friends, Dr. Don Bricker and James Arnold, Director of the Covenant Foundation at the time, to discuss with Dr. Isom some fundraising opportunities in New York City for our foundation, and out of that effort we wanted to establish the Isom Heart Center for Children at Covenant Children's Hospital. Dr. Isom took us out to dinner that first evening and he said to me, "Bob, I just want you to know that I've been a fan of yours long before you became a fan of mine." I said that I didn't know what he was talking about, and that I didn't know I had any fans except my two little doggies, Toto and Fancy Pants. He went on to say that when I first came to Lubbock to start my surgical practice that he was working at Methodist Hospital as a lab technician on the night shift from 11 p.m. to 7 a.m., and would frequently run into me at 2 or 3 o'clock in the morning as he was drawing blood on some emergency patients of mine. As the newest, youngest surgeon in town, the older surgeons were most happy to have the younger guy see most of the middle of the night surgical emergencies, so I was at the hospital frequently taking care of emergencies in the middle of the night. So, Dr. Isom went on to say that at 3 o'clock in the morning you find out real quickly who the nice guys are and who the a--h---s are. He wanted me to know that he always remembered that I was one of the nice guys.

The following year when he was a freshman medical student at Southwestern in Dallas, he had heard that I had operated successfully on a neighbor and friend of the Isom family for a complicated ruptured abdominal aortic aneurysm, the first of its kind in West Texas, and he said to himself, "Well, by damn, if Bob Salem from little Sudan, Texas, can do this kind of surgery, then so can Wayne Isom from Idalou, Texas." So, he had remembered and been stimulated by these two incidents as he progressed through his training and subsequent illustrious career in New York City.

Needless to say, I was extremely flattered by his comments.

Isom Heart Center for Children

This was the first of several trips to New York City and our fundraising efforts were quite successful. When Dr. Isom came to Lubbock to present the DeBakey Lectureship in 2005, we also announced the establishment of the Isom Heart Center for Children. Through Dr. Isom's cooperation, he arranged for us to have discussions with the Larry King Cardiac Foundation to consider the establishment of a partnership between Covenant and the Larry King Cardiac Foundation.

Larry King, Jr.

Larry King, Jr. is the President of the Larry King Cardiac Foundation and on one of our trips to New York, Dr. Isom had arranged for me and Dr. Ray Farmer, the Chief Medical Officer of Covenant Children's Hospital and my long-time good friend, to have a luncheon meeting with Larry, Jr. to begin to lay the foundation for this partnership between Covenant and the Larry King Cardiac Foundation. Larry King, Jr. was most accommodating with these efforts, made a couple of trips to Lubbock to look over our facilities, and then details of the partnership were solidified.

Cardiac Foundation Partnership

So, then in December 2007 we had the formal dedication of the Isom Heart Center, and Larry King and Larry King, Jr. made personal appearances in Lubbock for this dedication and also for a fundraising effort, at which time we announced the formation of this partnership, the funds of which will help to defray hospital costs for unfunded pediatric heart surgical patients. Larry King's wife, Shawn, eloquently made the formal announcement that evening at an elaborate affair at the Lubbock Country Club.

Larry King

The fundraiser was a spectacular event featuring the man himself, Larry King. I referred to him as the only man I knew who had more pairs of suspenders than my wife Kay has pairs of shoes. Larry is a unique and highly acclaimed talent. As host of the Larry King Live TV talk show, he is a master at interactive dialogue. The casual, comfortable, and intelligent manner in which he stimulates conversation with his guests is remarkable. I am amazed at how he navigates through his discussion night after night with such high-profile guests, and his broad base of knowledge on almost any subject is truly impressive. He is also one of Dr. Isom's many patients who have benefited from cardiac surgery. He and Dr. Isom presented a lively program with an informal dialogue of a litany of anecdotal events, and then they were joined by Bob Knight, Head Basketball Coach at Texas Tech University, who, in his traditional fashion, added additional candor and humor to the discussions.

At this stupendous event that evening, the Lt. Governor of Texas, David Dewhurst, presented Larry with a certificate making him an "Honorary Citizen of Texas," to the thunderous applause of everyone.

So, this was a great night for Covenant, for Lubbock, and particularly for the children of this area who will reap the most benefit from this partnership.

Walter Cronkite

Another person in New York City who was so very supportive of Covenant Health System was Walter Cronkite, a CBS anchor for many years and the most respected newscaster in the history of the medium. He was also a patient of Dr. Isom. His Chief of Staff, Marlene Adler, is one of the most charming and considerate people I've ever known, and helped tremendously in arranging for our interactions with Mr. Cronkite.

We had prepared a script for Mr. Cronkite to make, promoting

Covenant Health System, and on one of our trips to New York met him in a recording studio in midtown Manhattan for him to do the recording. He reviewed the script, altered the sentence structure a bit to fit his speaking style, sat down at the microphone and in one unrehearsed recording, produced the tape without a single stutter or flaw. The recording technician said that no one in the world but Mr. Cronkite could do such a perfect recording on the first attempt. His speaking style is so distinct and articulate that when anyone hears his voice, you don't have to ask, "Who is that talking?" – You immediately know it's Walter Cronkite.

On one trip we had discussed with him his coming to Lubbock with Dr. Isom to do a fundraising event for Covenant. He had agreed to do so and we had promoted this and had a sold out event billed as "An Evening With Walter Cronkite." One evening a few days before the event, Marlene called me to say that Mr. Cronkite's beloved wife, Betsy, had become seriously ill and he would have to cancel his engagement with us. A few days later we were saddened to learn of Mrs. Cronkite's death. I will always be grateful to Mrs. Adler and Mr. Cronkite for their time and genuine interest in supporting Covenant Health System.

As I was completing this manuscript, I learned of the death of Mr. Cronkite. During the ensuing days, I have never witnessed such an incredible outpouring of eulogies from every sector of our country – all extolling the lifetime of accomplishments and good works of this remarkable man. All newspapers and television stations continually expressed the heartfelt loss of one of our nation's most respected and revered citizens. In fact, I would go so far as to say that I know of no one in my lifetime who has commanded more esteem and admiration than he.

I remember so clearly that he was the first to report on TV, with his distinguished and eloquent speaking style, the assassination of President John Kennedy in 1963 and then Neil Armstrong's first steps on the moon in 1969. What a privilege it has been for me to have had a personal relationship with him and Marlene these past few years in NYC.

Doctors Salem,
Isom & Bricker

Doctors Bricker,
Isom & Salem

Dr. Isom,
Larry King,
Dr. Salem

Dedication Isom Heart Center

Dedication
Isom Heart
Center

Larry King
Family with
Dr. Isom

Larry King
Family with
Isoms & Salems

Kay & Dr. Salem
with Larry King

Dr. Salem,
Kay Salem,
Larry King,
and Shawn King

Shawn King &
Larry King
with Dr. John
Baldwin

110

Marty Zeiger
(Larry's Brother)
with Ellen
Zeiger and
the Kings

Dr. Isom,
Marty Zeiger,
Larry King, and
Dr. Salem

Larry King and
Lt. Governor
Dewhurst

Lt. Governor
Dewhurst and
Dr. Salem

Dr. Isom and
Larry King

Dr. Isom,
Larry King,
Bobby Knight

Larry King, Jr.,
Larry King,
Bobby Knight,
Dr. Isom

Senator Duncan,
Gwen Stafford,
Lt. Governor
Dewhurst

Denise Brunner,
Dr. Salem

113

Sharyn and
Royce Ivory

Kay Salem
and
Walter Cronkite

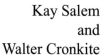

Walter Cronkite
and Dr. Salem

9

COVENANT HEART INSTITUTE
MICHAEL E. DEBAKEY, MD
DISTINGUISHED LECTURESHIP SERIES

Dr. Michael E. "Mike" DeBakey – Houston, TX – 2004

In 2004 I asked Dr. DeBakey if he would partner with Covenant in developing a distinguished lectureship series bearing his and Covenant's name. He readily agreed to do this, always willing to support his former residents any way he could. This lectureship series was to be an annual event, bringing in some of the most outstanding physicians and surgeons in the world today to help inform the people of West Texas and this area of the latest information in the field of Cardiology and Cardiovascular Surgery.

We asked Dr. DeBakey if he would give the inaugural address in 2004, which he did in remarkable fashion. The following is my introduction of him at that meeting:

DeBakey Introduction

Covenant Heart Institute
Dr. Michael E. DeBakey Distinguished
Lectureship Series

Lubbock, Texas

March 19, 2004

by: *[signature]*

Robert J. Salem, M.D., F.A.C.S.

115

One of the most difficult tasks I have had in a long time is trying to condense into a few minutes the astonishing and remarkable accomplishments of our guest speaker, spanning over 70 years of active surgical practice, but I have tried to capture some of the highlights.

- Internationally recognized as a *medical inventor*, a *dedicated teacher*, a *premier surgeon* and a *medical statesman*, Dr. DeBakey has changed the world's understanding of the heart.

- Currently the director of the DeBakey Heart Center, established by Baylor College of Medicine in partnership with Methodist Hospital, in Houston, Dr. DeBakey has served Baylor for most of his career, including as President from 1969-1979 and as Chancellor from 1979 – 1996.

- A native of Louisiana, he began his career at Tulane in 1937, and subsequently volunteered for military service in World War II.

- Later while serving as a director in the Surgeon General's office, he helped develop mobile army surgical hospitals, which we commonly recognize as MASH units.

- His *scientific achievements* are numerous:

  - While in medical school he invented the roller pump, which became a major component of the heart lung machine, which takes over the function of the heart and lungs during surgery.

  - In the 50's he developed dacron artificial grafts to replace diseased arteries in many parts of the body.

116

- In 1964 he performed the first successful coronary artery by-pass using a large vein removed from the leg to bypass obstructed areas in the coronary artery. Thousands of this life saving operation are now being performed annually throughout the world.

- His early research in the 60's with the *artificial* heart and his testimony before Congress, led to federal support of the artificial heart program in this country.

- His most recent innovation that is receiving world wide attention and acclaim is the *DeBakey VAD(Ventricular Assist Device)*, a *heart pump* to support failing hearts – the subject of his presentation today. This device was developed through decades of research in conjunction with NASA engineers and employs aspects of space technology.

- Dr. DeBakey has been a *medical statesman* for half a century, serving as an advisor to almost every President in the late 20th century and to heads of state throughout the world.

- In 1996 he served as consultant to physicians treating President Boris Yelstin in Moscow for a heart attack.

- He is a prolific writer and has authored more than one thousand four hundred articles, chapters and books on *surgery, medicine, health, medical research* and *medical education*, as well as *ethical, socio-economic and philosophical issues.*

- He has performed more than 60,000 cardiovascular surgical procedures and has trained thousands of surgeons world wide, including several of us here at Covenant.

- His dedication to the training of young physicians and researchers and his keen intellect and devotion to the service of humanity, have made him a legend in his own time.

- Everyone of us who has worked side by side with him stand in awe and bewilderment of his incomparable _stamina, drive_ and _intensity_.

- He taught by example and among the many things he taught us, two things stand out uppermost in my mind.

- The first is his total commitment to excellence and perfection – every detail must be well thought out – every movement of the hands must be purposeful and every stitch must be perfectly placed. Anything short of absolute perfection was simply not acceptable.

- The second thing we learned from Dr. DeBakey was what a hard work ethic really meant – 20 hour days, 7 days a week, were the norm and frequently they were 24 hour days; and to this day he keeps up such a fast paced, rigorous schedule all over the world that few, if any of us, could follow in his steps.

- With all of his remarkable accomplishments, Dr. DeBakey is widely recognized as "The Father of Heart Care" and he is acclaimed as the *most renowned physician and surgeon in the world today*. His legacy is unparalleled and historians will no doubt record him as being one of the *giants of the 20th century* and *yes, of all time*.

Ladies and Gentlemen –

Dr. Michael DeBakey

At age 95, he came to the podium and delivered the most eloquent and erudite address imaginable utilizing his own PowerPoint presentation. After his formal presentation, he fielded impromptu questions from the floor for another 30 minutes, responding to each question in a clear, articulate and decisive manner. One question posed was to what did he attribute his remarkable longevity and maintenance of a sound mind. He responded with, "Well, the first thing is that I selected the right parents," emphasizing the hereditary and genetic importance of one's life and health, particularly in the cardiac area.

At the conclusion of his remarks, the audience of over 300 people erupted in thunderous applause that lasted for several minutes. To a person, everyone recognized that they had just witnessed a momentous piece of history.

Every year since then we have brought in longtime acquaintances who have distinguished themselves in the field of Cardiothoracic Surgery and who have received national and international recognition and notoriety. The list is as follows:

2004 – Dr. Michael E. DeBakey of Houston, Texas
2005 – Dr. Wayne Isom of New York City
2006 – Dr. George Noon of Houston, Texas

2007 – Dr. John Ochsner of New Orleans, Louisiana
2008 – Dr. Ted Diethrich of Phoenix, Arizona
2009 – Dr. Ken Mattox of Houston, Texas
2010 – Dr. Denton Cooley of Houston, Texas

It took me many years before I could forget the physically and emotionally demanding rigors of the DeBakey residency years. Reflectively, as I began to reminisce over the remarkable training experience I had received with Dr. DeBakey that held me in such good stead as I began my surgical practice, I began to comprehend and appreciate the unique opportunity I was so fortunate to have had. Then I began to love and revere him. During the past 20 years I've learned to value and understand his method of teaching, which few, if any, surgical mentors demonstrate today. I started making frequent trips to Houston just to visit with him in his office, which were facilitated by his wonderful and loyal staff—Henny Banning, Brenda Thomlinson and Mike Richardson. And the more I saw him, the more I learned about his more intimate personal self. I learned for the first time that his father was a Lebanese immigrant, as was mine. I learned that he was valedictorian of his high school class, as was I. I learned that he played the saxophone as a youth, as did I. I learned that he had a staunch and firm belief in God, as do I. I learned that he was a deeply sentimental and compassionate human being that I had not appreciated in the years of my training and for several years afterwards.

One of the great stories about Dr. DeBakey's life had to do with his care of Boris Yeltsin, first president of Russia in the post-Soviet era. President Yeltsin had had a heart attack and was having continued anginal heart pain and it was felt that he needed a coronary bypass operation, but his Russian physicians did not feel that he could survive the operation.

So, President Yeltsin consulted Dr. DeBakey directly who agreed to come to Moscow to evaluate the President. After his evaluation, Dr. DeBakey felt that Mr. Yeltsin could indeed, in all probability, survive the operation, but only after proper preoperative management to include treatment of an anemia and low thyroid function. So surgery was delayed until these problems were treated and then surgery, a quadruple coronary artery bypass was successfully done several weeks later by a Russian cardiovascular surgeon, Dr. Renat A. Akchurin. As agreed upon earlier, Dr. DeBakey and his associate, Dr. George Noon, returned to Moscow for the surgery and were present in the O.R. for consultation and advice during the procedure. Boris did well following surgery and lived ten more productive years, and Dr. DeBakey was given a lot of credit for this good result, which allowed President Yeltsin to continue to lead Russia and subsequently handpick his successor, Vladimir Putin.

DeBakey made more than 20 trips to Russia in his career and is held in high esteem by the Kremlin, and Mr. Yeltsin has described him as "a magician of the heart" and "a man with a gift for performing miracles."

Dr. DeBakey introduced me to the Russian heart surgeon, Dr. Akchurin, a couple of years ago in Houston. He speaks excellent English and extended me an invitation to visit him at his hospital in Moscow sometime – haven't made it back to Moscow – maybe someday.

One of the greatest honors I've received in my life was Dr. DeBakey's invitation, extended through his nurse, Henny Banning, to attend the Congressional Gold Medal Ceremony in his honor in the Rotunda of the Capitol in Washington D.C. on April 23, 2008. This is the highest civilian award given by our Congress, and it was presented personally by President George W. Bush. As I sat there in the Rotunda with my lifetime of memories of Dr. DeBakey ricocheting off those hallowed walls, and with the United States Army Chorus providing musical selections in the background, I had this overwhelming feeling of immense pride for Dr. DeBakey and his being awarded our nation's most prestigious civilian award for his lifetime of unparalleled accomplishments in the Cardiovascular world of Medicine, benefitting all mankind.

The program participants other than President Bush and Dr. DeBakey included the Speaker of the House of Representatives, the Honorable Nancy Pelosi, and the Majority Leader of the Senate, the Honorable Harry Reid. Several other members of Congress were in attendance and participated in the ceremony, including the Honorable Kay Bailey Hutchinson, United States Senator from Texas; the Honorable Al Green, United States Representative from the Ninth District of Texas; the Honorable John Boehner, Republican Leader of the House of Representatives and the Honorable Mitch McConnell, Republican Leader of the United States Senate. In closing the ceremony,

Dr. DeBakey gave a wonderful acceptance speech with words of thanks and also made a few suggestions to the people in attendance regarding the delivery of healthcare in the country.

This award was first given to George Washington in 1776 and originally was bestowed upon distinguished military leaders, but over the decades has been given to diverse individuals, including notables in science and medicine. Dr. DeBakey is one of only a handful of physicians who have received this award since its inception.

The Congressional Gold Medal is designed specifically and uniquely for each individual recipient. In Dr. DeBakey's case, on one side it depicts Dr. DeBakey in his typical operative scrubs with an operating table in the background. And then the opposite side features a replica of the heart overlaid on a world globe, depicting Dr. DeBakey's worldwide influence and the teaching of cardiovascular procedures to surgeons all around the world. Also prominently displayed is a DeBakey quote, "The Pursuit Of Excellence Has Been My Objective In Life."

Baylor College of Medicine hosted a reception in the Library of Congress following the ceremony, which Dr. DeBakey attended. He greeted well wishers for several hours while photographs were made. He was 99 years old at the time and his encyclopedic, intellectual mind, memory and recall were just as sharp and crisp as they ever were.

While I was there attending this spectacular event in Washington, I had the opportunity to reminisce with my good friend Dr. Charles McCollum. Charley was one of the outstanding junior residents working under me, referred to earlier, when I was Chief. After completion of his residency, he stayed on the faculty and worked with Dr. DeBakey throughout his career. Dr. McCollum would, a few months later, present a stirring tribute and memorial to Dr. DeBakey at the Texas Surgical Society meeting in San Antonio in September, 2008.

Also, Dr. Cooley was present for Dr. DeBakey's Congressional Gold Medal Award Ceremony and I had the opportunity to visit with him again along with Dr. Bud Frazier, renowned for his work at the Texas Heart Institute in cardiac transplantation.

On the evening of July 11, 2008, just two months short of his 100th birthday, and three months after the Congressional Gold Medal Ceremony, the life and career of one of the most incredible physicians and human beings of the centuries past came to a sudden but climatic end. I had just called his office that morning and was told that he was already home, and rather than bother him at home I left word for him to call me the following Monday to set up a time for me to visit him again in Houston. That Friday evening he had had dinner and later on had a sudden cardiac event that ended his life.

On July 15, 2008, he lay in repose at City Hall in Houston, the first time the 67-year-old government building had been used to pay tribute to one of Houston's residents. This one-of-a-kind public viewing was felt to be an appropriate honor, given Dr. DeBakey's contributions to the city of Houston and modern medicine.

I was asked by his staff to take a turn for two hours to stand guard by his open casket along with the military honor guard, which I readily accepted.

He was appropriately dressed in hospital attire because that is the dress most people remember him in – scrub suit, white coat, cloth surgical cap and mask pulled down from his face in a position familiar to thousands he had discussed surgical events with, and a stethoscope draped around his neck.

Thousands came by for the viewing and attended the memorial service the next day at Co-Cathedral of the Sacred Heart in Houston. He later received a full military burial at Arlington Cemetery, having served as a Lieutenant Colonel in the Army Surgeon's Office during WW II. Thus ended a 50-year relationship, but the memories of the "DeBakey Factor" will linger with me for the remaining years of my life.

Dr. DeBakey was internationally recognized as a dedicated teacher, premier surgeon, medical inventor and statesman. He is acclaimed as one of the most renowned physicians and surgeons in the world. His legacy is unparalleled and historians will no doubt record him as being one of the Giants of the 20th Century and, yes, of all time. To this very day I still feel a huge void in my life and my heart, but I am so grateful for the experiences I had with this most remarkable person. In spite of his death, the " DeBakey Factor" will remain with me for the duration of my life.

Dr. Wayne Isom – New York City, New York - 2005

In 1985 Dr. Isom, whom we've already talked about earlier, was recruited to New York Presbyterian–Weill Cornell and was appointed

Chief of the Division of Cardiovascular Surgery at that time. He is the recipient of numerous prestigious awards and has had a highly successful career in New York City. His presentation for the 2005 DeBakey Lectureship was about the heart/lung machine, and he showed film clips on some of the celebrities he has operated upon in New York including Larry King, Walter Cronkite and David Letterman. His career has been an illustrious one, and West Texas is proud to claim him as a native son.

Dr. George Noon – Houston, Texas – 2006

Dr. Noon was a junior resident under me at the time of my residency at the same time as Dr. Bricker and Dr McCollum. He was head of the heart transplant program and worked with Dr. DeBakey throughout his entire career. At the 2006 DeBakey Lectureship, Dr. Noon talked about cardiac transplantation and cardiac-assist devices. In 2007 Dr. Noon received national and international acclaim and notoriety for performing a successful operation on Dr. DeBakey at age 97 for a dissection aneurysm of his thoracic aorta, a condition that Dr. DeBakey had described many years earlier.

Dr. Noon had been consulted about Dr. DeBakey's aneurysm shortly after Dr. DeBakey was admitted to Methodist Hospital in Houston. Dr. DeBakey initially did not want to consider surgery, and I feel sure that Dr. Noon did not relish the thought of doing surgery of this kind on a 97-year-old patient, which on someone half this age carries with it a significant morbidity and mortality, and especially on doing this on such a high-profile person as Dr. DeBakey. I mean, man, it doesn't get any higher profile than he!

So, they watched the aneurysm as it gradually expanded and rupture, and sudden death appeared imminent. Finally a decision was made between Dr. and Mrs. DeBakey, Dr. Noon and the Ethics Committee of the hospital to perform the surgery. But then there was the question of the anesthetic – who was going to administer the anesthetic? I'm sure there weren't a lot of anesthesiologists lining up to give this high-profile, high-risk patient an anesthetic because I feel reasonably certain that most of them would not expect him to survive and no one wanted on their resume, "I bumped off Mike DeBakey."

Well, Dr. Noon found someone to give the anesthetic and

124

courageously performed the surgery successfully. He had a long and protracted postoperative course and recovery, but eventually did recover, his brain and intellect perfectly intact, and he had many more months of productive activity thereafter.

In my mind, this is one of the most heroic operations and post operative recoveries in the Annals of Surgery, and give credit to the patient and all the doctors and hospital staff who attended him for this most remarkable and incredulous story.

Dr. John Ochsner – New Orleans, Louisiana – 2007

Dr. John Ochsner is one of the most renowned surgeons of our time. After completing his thoracic and cardiovascular training with Dr. DeBakey, he returned to practice thoracic and cardiovascular surgery in New Orleans at the Ochsner Hospital, which his father had founded, and at Tulane in New Orleans. Dr. John Ochsner's father was Dr. Alton Ochsner, who is given credit for defining the relationship between cigarette smoking and lung cancer. I had Dr. Alton Ochsner come to Lubbock in 1975 to give the commencement address to the first graduating class of the Texas Tech Medical School. He actually trained Dr. DeBakey in his early years at Tulane in New Orleans, and then many years later sent John to train with Dr. DeBakey in Houston. The two families had a close personal as well as professional relationship for many decades.

In the early days when Dr. DeBakey was doing his early training in New Orleans, Dr. DeBakey would babysit John and his siblings when Dr. and Mrs. Alton Ochsner were away, so that there was always this extreme closeness and bonding of the Ochsner and DeBakey families.

At the 2007 DeBakey Lectureship Dr. Ochsner talked about the modern day spinoffs from cardiovascular surgery. He and Dr. Noon both spoke at Dr. DeBakey's memorial service in Houston.

Dr. Ted Diethrich – Phoenix, Arizona – 2008

Dr. Diethrich founded the Arizona Heart Institute in Phoenix, and also received his thoracic and cardiovascular training with Dr. DeBakey. He stayed on the staff with Dr. DeBakey at Baylor for several years prior to going to Phoenix. He, like the other previous distinguished lecturers, is internationally recognized and renowned as one of the leading surgeons in the world with the use of endovascular stents (placing of a graft inside a diseased artery by catheters inserted, usually in the groin, without the necessity of a major open operation). He is a much sought-after speaker at seminars worldwide and made an incredibly outstanding presentation on the impact of "The DeBakey Era" on cardiovascular care in the future and his vision for the treatment of heart patients, explaining future technologies, techniques and bioscience and genetic implications.

Dr. Ken Mattox – Houston, Texas – 2009

Dr. Mattox is one of the world's leading and most highly respected trauma surgeons. He moved to Houston for his medical school training at Baylor and remained there for the rest of his professional surgical career, working with Dr. DeBakey on the Baylor faculty, but carving out his own international reputation as an innovator in the treatment of trauma. Dr. Mattox revered Dr. DeBakey, as Dr. DeBakey did him. He is one of the highest profiled surgeons in the world today, and he wrote the lead article in the Texas Medicine Journal in September 2008 about Dr. DeBakey entitled, "Tribute to a Legend." He wrote that the "Texas Tornado" continues to cast a long shadow and has left large boot prints for us to follow for many decades to come.

Dr. Mattox, who casts his own tall shadow in the surgical world, made a presentation on the impact of trauma, war and disaster on society, which was a resounding success and warmly received and appreciated by all in attendance.

Dr. Mattox was the first to call me about Dr. DeBakey's death, and spent many hours shortly after the event notifying Dr. DeBakey's friends and colleagues around the world.

Dr. Denton Cooley – Houston, Texas – 2010

Dr. Cooley is a native Texan, born and raised in Houston. He attended the University of Texas, where he distinguished himself academically and athletically.

He completed his surgical residency with Dr. Alfred Blalock, professor and Chair of Surgery at Johns Hopkins University, Baltimore, Maryland. While there as an intern, he participated in the first "blue baby" operation ever done in the world performed by Dr. Blalock, which led later on to his own pioneering work on infants with congenital heart anomalies.

Dr. DeBakey recruited Dr. Cooley to join him on the full-time faculty of Baylor College of Medicine as Vice-Chairman of the Department of Surgery in 1951.

So when I arrived to start my surgical training in 1958, I would have the unique opportunity to observe and work with two of the most renowned cardiovascular surgeons in the history of the world.

Dr. Cooley is by all historians one of the greatest cardiovascular surgeons of our time and perhaps of all time. Because of his unique stature in the surgical world, comparable to Dr. DeBakey, I had wanted to extend him an invitation to participate in the lectureship series shortly after Dr. DeBakey. But because of the distant relationship between the two at the time, I, on the advice of others who knew them both, was reluctant to do so. But over the past two years, a reconciliation of the two greatest cardiovascular surgeons in the world occurred. Dr. Cooley took the first step and presented Dr. DeBakey with a lifetime achievement award from the Cooley Cardiovascular Surgical Society and then six months later, on May 3, 2008, DeBakey inducted Cooley into the DeBakey International Surgical Society, which I attended.

In the Houston Chronicle of May 8, 2008, Cooley was quoted as saying about the historic reconciliation, "The rivalry will go down as one of the greatest rivalries in modern medicine. I'm relieved we are again together and can be colleagues and friends again."

Dr. DeBakey was quoted in the same article, "Denton, it's a great pleasure for me to acknowledge the pioneering contributions you have made and have you a part of the society. I don't think I could have done it without (you). In fact, I know I couldn't."

The feud had lasted for decades, but suddenly these two legendary heart surgeons seemed thick as thieves.

Dr. Ken Mattox would say, "You can see the bonds. They sat at the table chatting away like old friends who'd had memorable fishing or hunting trips together."

It was truly a memorable experience and event in my life and having lived a lifetime of my own with these two legendary men in my background, I still revel in the moment of one of medicine's most bodacious events.

At the lectureship in March 2010, Dr. Cooley will talk about the development of the Texas Heart Institute and congenital heart anomalies.

So, this distinguished lectureship series has attracted to date seven of the most highly regarded surgeons in the world, and has afforded the people of West Texas a unique experience in hearing outstanding presentations on a variety of subjects, but also an equally unique opportunity to meet and interact on an informal personal level with the finest in the world.

2004 DeBakey Lectureship
Dr. Michael E. DeBakey

Surgeons
with
Dr. DeBakey

Doctors Bricker,
DeBakey and
Salem

Doctors Salem
and DeBakey
with Kay

To Erica – Best Wishes
Michael E. DeBakey

Erica Stevens
(Dr. Salem's
Granddaughter)
with Doctors
DeBakey and
Salem

Doctors
Mangold,
DeBakey and
Salem

Doctors
DeBakey
and Allen

Dr. and Mrs.
Salem, Dr. and
Mrs. Harrell with
Dr. DeBakey

Dr. and Mrs.
Bricker with
Dr. DeBakey

Dr. Selby
and
Dr. DeBakey

Dr. and Mrs.
Hansen with
Dr. DeBakey

Delwin Jones
with Dr.
DeBakey

Dr. Bricker,
Dr. Salem,
Charley Trimble
with Dr. DeBakey

132

Dr. & Mrs.
Salem with
Dr. DeBakey

Dr. and Mrs.
Thomas with
Dr. DeBakey

Dr. Horton
with Doctors
DeBakey and
Salem

Dr. Salem and Dr. DeBakey

President Boris Yelstin and Dr. DeBakey

CONGRESSIONAL GOLD MEDAL CEREMONY

in honor of

MICHAEL ELLIS DEBAKEY, M.D.

The Rotunda
United States Capitol
Wednesday, April 23, 2008
11:00 a.m.

Program

Prelude
The United States Army Chorus

Welcome
The Honorable Nancy Pelosi, *The Speaker of the United States House of Representatives*

Presentation of the Colors
The United States Armed Forces Color Guard

National Anthem
The United States Army Chorus

Invocation
The Reverend Daniel Coughlin, *Chaplain of the United States House of Representatives*

Remarks on the Resolution
The Honorable Kay Bailey Hutchison, *United States Senate, Texas*
The Honorable Al Green, *United States House of Representatives, Ninth District of Texas*

Musical Selection
The United States Army Chorus

Remarks
The Honorable John Boehner, *Republican Leader of the United States*
House of Representatives
The Honorable Mitch McConnell, *Republican Leader of the United States Senate*
The Honorable Harry Reid, *Majority Leader of the United States Senate*
The Honorable Nancy Pelosi, *The Speaker of the United States House of Representatives*
The Honorable George W. Bush, *The President of the United States*

Presentation of the Congressional Gold Medal
The Honorable Harry Reid, *Majority Leader of the United States Senate*
The Honorable Nancy Pelosi, *The Speaker of the United States House of Representatives*
The Honorable George W. Bush, *The President of the United States*

Acceptance and Word of Thanks
Michael Ellis DeBakey, M.D.

Benediction
The Reverend Barry Black, *Chaplain of the United States Senate*

Doctors
Frazier, Salem,
and Cooley

Doctors
McCollum,
Frazier, and
Cooley

Congressional
Gold Medal
(Dr. Salem and
Dr. DeBakey)

Congressional
Gold Medal
(Dr. Salem and
Dr. DeBakey)

Dr. DeBakey

MICHAEL E. DeBAKEY
1908 - 2008

2005 DeBakey Lectureship
Dr. Wayne Isom

Dr. Wayne Isom

Doctors Salem and Isom

Pat and Wayne
Isom

Dr. Isom
with
Surgeons

Dr. Paul Walter
and Dr. Isom

Doctors Bricker, Isom, Harrell and Salem

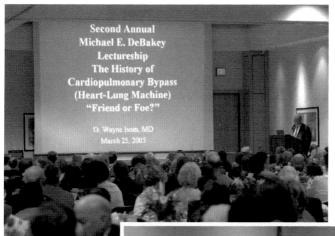

Isom
Program
Photo

Doctors
Isom, King
and Henry

Isoms
and
Salems

Wanda Becknell,
Lexie Isom,
and Brenda
Becknell

2006 DeBakey Lectureship
Dr. George Noon

Dr. George Noon

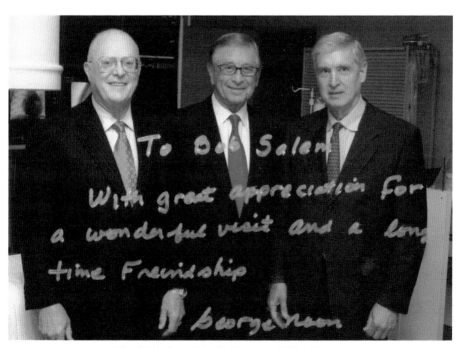

Dr. Bricker, Dr. Salem and Dr. Noon

Dr. Salem
and Dr. Noon

Dr. Noon and
Cathy Porter

Sharon Prather
and Dr. Noon

144

Dr. Allen
and Dr. Noon

Doctors Salem,
Noon and
Harrell

Brickers
and
Salems with
Dr. Noon

Doctors Noon, DeBakey and Salem

Doctors DeBakey and Salem

146

2007 DeBakey Lectureship
Dr. John Ochsner

Dr. John Ochsner

Dr. Ochsner
and Dr. Salem

Doctors Salem,
Ochsner and
Bale

Dr. Rhyne
and
Dr. Ochsner

Dr. Ochsner
and Kay

Dr. Ochsner,
Kay and
Dr. Salem

Dr. Harrell
and
Dr. Ochsner

Dr. Salem and
Dr. Ochsner
with DeBakey
Medallion

Dr. Ochsner at
Presentation

2008 DeBakey Lectureship
Dr. Ted Diethrich

Dr. Ted Diethrich

Dr. Diethrich and Dr. Salem

Dr. Diethrich,
Kay and
Dr. Salem

Dr. Diethrich,
Pat and Danny
Johnston

Doctors
Springer,
Diethrich,
and Harrell

151

Doctors Springer, Harrell, Diethrich, Salem, Horton and Cathy Porter

Slide Presentation

2009 DeBakey Lectureship
Dr. Ken Mattox

Dr. Ken Mattox

Dr. Mattox and Dr. Rosen

Dr. Mattox
with Cath Lab
Crew

Dr. Mattox
and Dr.
Levine

Dr. Mattox
and
Greg Jones

Donna Griffis,
Karen Worley,
and Kay Salem

Doctors
Mattox,
Harrell, Salem
with TTUHSC
Residents

Dr. Salem
and Dr. Mattox

Dr. Salem and
Dr. Mattox
with DeBakey
Medallion

Dr. Mattox
with Kay and
Dr. Salem

Dr. Mattox
and
Dr. Zias

2010 DeBakey Lectureship
Dr. Denton Cooley

Doctors Salem and Cooley

GOOD FRIENDS: Dr. Denton Cooley, left, and Dr. Michael DeBakey exchanged pleasantries Friday during Cooley's induction into DeBakey's surgical society. Watch the ceremony as the legendary heart surgeons discuss an end to their rivalry and their renewed friendship at **chron.com/metro.**

STEVE UECKERT : CHRONICLE

Bond between top surgeons grows

■ **Amid praise, DeBakey inducts Cooley into his surgical society**

By TODD ACKERMAN
HOUSTON CHRONICLE

They feuded for decades, but legendary heart surgeons Dr. Michael DeBakey and Dr. Denton Cooley suddenly seem thick as thieves.

Six months after Cooley's cardiovascular surgical society presented DeBakey with a lifetime achievement award, De-Bakey repaid the honor Friday, inducting Cooley into his own surgical society and lauding his contribution to modern medicine.

"Denton, it's a great pleasure for me to acknowledge the pioneering contributions you have made and have you a part of the society," said DeBakey, 99. "I don't think I could have done it

"You can see the bond. They sat at the table chatting away like old friends who'd had memorable fishing or hunting trips together."
—DR. KENNETH MATTOX,
secretary-treasurer of the Michael E. DeBakey International Surgical Society

without (you). In fact, I know I couldn't."

Cooley, 87, responded that he thought the pair's "rivalry will go down in history as one of the greatest rivalries in modern medicine. I'm relieved we are again together and can be colleagues and friends again."

'Chatting away'

Following the induction, Cooley changed his plans to head home after DeBakey asked him to come to the meeting's luncheon and sit next to him, said Dr. Kenneth Mattox, secretary-treasurer of the Michael E. DeBakey International Surgical Society and surgeon-in-chief at Ben Taub General Hospital.

"It's definitely real," Mattox said of their new relationship. "You can see the bond. They sat at the table chatting away like old friends who'd had memorable fishing or hunting trips together."

For more than four decades, DeBakey and Cooley seemed nothing like old friends. Theirs was one of modern medicine's best-known feuds, a falling-out

that spurred both to greater heights, divided a community and eventually became the stuff of legend.

It began, quietly, in 1960, when the two proved to be temperamentally incompatible and Cooley left DeBakey's operation at Methodist Hospital to start his own practice down the street at St. Luke's Episcopal Hospital. Two years later, he founded the Texas Heart Institute.

The rift blew up in 1969, when Cooley performed the world's first artificial heart implant, without permission using a mechanical device developed in DeBakey's lab.

Cooley was censured by the American College of Surgeons and resigned from the faculty at Baylor College of Medicine. On the rare occasions he and De-Bakey found themselves in the same room, the two usually avoided each other.

But last October, the two finally ended the feud. At a meeting of the Denton A. Cooley Cardiovascular Society at which no advance notice was given of the plan in case DeBakey didn't show up, Cooley inducted his

longtime rival into his society. The meeting drew a prolonged standing ovation from the surgeons in attendance.

Talking about the past

Friday's moment was less dramatic, mostly because those in attendance knew it was on the agenda all along. The society's 17th biennial meeting drew about 400 surgeons, who got their first chance to see De-Bakey since his life-threatening aortic aneurysm caused him to miss the 2006 event.

DeBakey and Cooley reminisced about their years together at Baylor in the 1950s, when the two pioneered treatment of aortic aneurysms, work that would save DeBakey half a century later. DeBakey said Cooley had the "instincts of a great surgeon" and said they "complemented each other and worked together very effectively."

Cooley said the competition between the two programs was the stimulus for many new developments, then added it would be interesting to "see what harmony will do. Unfortunately, for both of us, the end is in sight."

Friday's event came a week after DeBakey was given the Congressional Gold Medal, Congress' highest civilian award. Cooley traveled to Washington to attend the ceremony.

todd.ackerman@chron.com

158

10
THE BEST OF LIFE

One of the best things Kay and I have done in our lives has been to travel, especially to foreign countries. As a young girl, Kay had traveled extensively with her grandparents, and I had developed a taste for foreign travel during my Air Force years in Europe, so we both have enjoyed this activity very much.

Flight to Moscow

We have made trips to Athens and the Greek Islands, Istanbul, Vienna, Paris, London, Venice, Budapest, Rome, China, Prague, Switzerland, Russia, Germany, Sweden and others. One of our most memorable was on one of our cruises in 2000. We were anchored in St. Petersburg, Russia, for three days and on the second day there had the option of flying to Moscow for the day on a Russian Aeroflot flight. We were a little bit skeptical and anxious about taking a Russian Aeroflot airplane because in the backs of our minds we seemed to have remembered that maybe they didn't have the safety records of some other airlines, but the excursion had been arranged by a most reputable cruise line and we finally decided that this would be a once-in-a-lifetime experience. We had read about Red Square and Stalin's tomb all of our lives, and to be this close and not take advantage of the opportunity to see these historical places prevailed over our anxieties.

British Airways Captain Allan and Liz Dobbie

It was to be an 18-hour day, so we arose early and of the 300 people on the cruise line, only about 30 of us were adventurous (or stupid) enough to make the trip. On arrival at the airport in St. Petersburg before dawn, we had time to grab a cup of coffee and mix and mingle. Kay, who has no problem mixing and mingling with strangers, immediately engaged in conversation with one charming English couple, Allan and Liz Dobbie. As it turns out, Liz is an attorney in England with a degree from Oxford and Allan is a senior captain for British Airways. So, we got instant relief of our anxieties in knowing that a British Airways senior pilot was taking the same flight we were to Moscow.

As we boarded the flight, we took our seats in the passenger

159

section, but Allan had prearranged for him to sit up in the cockpit with Russian pilots. After a few minutes into the flight, Allan comes back from the cockpit and sits down with Liz, Kay and me. We are all anxious to know how the flight was going and Allan, being the joker he is (but Kay and I didn't know it at the time) said, "Well, everybody start praying – they are up there communicating by Morse code" (an obsolete method of communicating years ago). This initially startled all of us, but he immediately said that he was just joking and that they had all of the modern technology that he had on his British Airways planes. We went on to have a pleasant, safe flight, and a memorable day in Moscow, ending with a vodka and Caviar, and beef stroganoff dinner at an elegant Russian dinner club, and a safe flight back to St. Petersburg late that night.

Flight to Prague

The next year, the summer before September 11, 2001, the Dobbies invited us over to visit them at their beautiful home in Oxford. We were there for a couple of days when they said they had arranged a surprise for us and to pack a bag for a couple of days for a short trip. Well, they had arranged for the four of us to take a British Airways flight to Prague for a two-day visit there.

After we were in flight from London to Prague, the stewardess comes to my seat and said that the Captain would like to see Dr. Salem in the cockpit. Well, I immediately thought he might be ill and need some medical attention, so I got right up and followed her to the cockpit. Upon arrival there, he said that Captain Dobbie had told him that I had had a lot of experience flying all over Europe, and to please sit down in the jump seat behind him and help him fly this thing to Prague. Well, Allan had arranged prior to the flight for me to have this experience, and what an experience it was! I put on the headphones and enjoyed all of the chatter that goes on between pilot and communications centers.

After a delightful two days touring Prague with Liz and Allan, we returned to London on another British Airways flight. On this flight Allan had arranged for me to sit in the jump seat again behind the pilot, but had also arranged for Kay to sit in the seat behind the co-pilot. So there we are – flying in the cockpit of a British Airways plane on the way from Prague to London. One gets such a spectacular view through the cockpit window - panoramic 180 degree view- and as we descended into London, the pilots pointed out to us the various famous London landmarks – London Bridge, Windsor Castle, Wimbledon Tennis Courts, and the like. This was another once-in-a-lifetime experience, just a few weeks before the terrorist attack on the World Trade Center Towers in New York City, and obviously no one will ever have an experience like that again. We have remained good friends with the Dobbies, have met them for visits in New York City twice, and Liz and Kay email several times weekly. Their son, Chris, whom we met on our visit, is a medic in the British Marines and is a handsome young man. Liz and Allan are justly quite proud of him.

Ms. Georgia Dingus – Language Professor at Texas Tech
Cicero and the Soul

A patient and friend of mine, Georgia Wilson Dingus, wrote and published a book in 1967 entitled, The Best of Life. She was a Language Professor at Texas Tech University and this book was her own translation from Latin into English of Cicero's essay On Old Age (De Senectute). I have read and re-read several times the signed copy she gave me following her breast cancer surgery in 1978, and glean more insight on living and dying each time I read it. This book, although written originally by Cicero shortly before the time of Christ, has many practical applications relevant in today's world regarding life, living and growing old. And I will always be grateful to her for sharing with me and thousands of others her perspective on Cicero's wonderful essay.

In the forward of the book, Mrs. Dingus says, "I know of no better source of practical and wholesome advice on living than Cicero's essay On Old Age (De Senectute). It should offer consolation to those dreading old age as well as to those who have already arrived there." She recounts some of her student's comments such as "I liked the essay On Old Age (De Senectute) best of all of Cicero's works, because it answers questions that need answers. I thought I would rather die young than to endure old age. Cicero has shown me there are pleasures in old age as well as in youth, and that death, whether one believes in immortality or not, is but the natural ending to long life."

She states further that, "The latter years of life should continue to be enjoyment and productive for each person" and shows people of all ages how to regard and obey the laws of nature with grace and admit that character, instead of age, accounts for our faults. In the book there are several references by Cicero to the "soul," which he says is evident in life even though it is invisible, and that we should believe, therefore, it continues to exist when the body is no longer visible.

He says, as translated by Mrs. Dingus, "Do not think, my dearest sons, that when I have left you I shall cease to exist. Even while I was with you, you did not see my soul; but you knew from my actions that it was in this body. Therefore you should believe that it continues to exist when you no longer see my body."

I find it most intriguing that Cicero's philosophical writings over 2,000 years ago regarding the soul and immortality parallel that of many major religious beliefs today. There are numerous references in the Bible, particular in John 3:16 and 36, and in John 6:40, and in John 11:25 and 26 regarding everlasting life. Astonishingly, in my view, they liken very much the views of Cicero, who died in 43 B.C.

As a surgeon in training in a high-volume trauma center in Houston, we had a little bit of a warped and perverted view about what and where the soul was. Dr. DeBakey and other trauma surgeons told us, facetiously, that the soul was located in the upper mid-abdomen toward the back near the abdominal aorta and pancreas, certainly anatomically one of the most difficult areas to access, and one of the most difficult to treat surgically. Injuries, particularly gunshot wounds and blunt abdominal trauma, in this area carry with them a very high morbidity and mortality. So, if one of us said to the other that we had treated a "soul shot," we immediately knew the type of serious injury that we had been treating. This was always said jestingly with tongue in cheek. This is the type of injury that Jack Ruby, the Dallas nightclub owner, inflicted upon Lee Harvey Oswald, who was accused of the assassination of President Kennedy in 1963 in Dallas.

But this most certainly was not the same "soul" that Cicero was referencing and undoubtedly believed in with all of his heart and philosophical mind.

As a Christian believer, I have often wondered why my life on numerous occasions had been spared. I've had multiple encounters, any of which could have snuffed out my life. My first as a young boy was encountered on a family vacation in the mountains in New Mexico. I was

162

thrown off a horse, sustaining a head injury rendering me unconscious, and I remember awakening and lying beside a mountain stream with my father and other adults applying cold water towels to my forehead.

I was really fortunate to have survived my teenage years in high school, having had three major accidents during those years. One was a car rollover, totaling my parents' only car as I was taking a date home one night, and two other head injuries, one sustained in a basketball game when I ran my head into the end of the gymnasium, and another during a football game when I was running in to block a PAT and the kicker missed the football and kicked me in the head instead. I woke up the next day in the hospital in Littlefield being treated by our family physician, Dr. Clifford Payne.

My years of private practice were interrupted by several more additional serious events. The first was surgery for a malignant melanoma, and at the time I felt I was destined for a bad outcome because nearly all of the patients I had seen at M.D. Anderson Hospital in Houston during my training as a resident who had malignant melanoma did not survive, nor did most of those I had treated myself in Lubbock. It was only after several years with no recurrence or metastasis that I felt that I had been cured. Then there was a snow skiing accident and yet another head injury, resulting in a subdural hematoma requiring surgery. Then, a thoracotomy for a suspected malignant lung lesion that was thought to be a primary lung cancer or metastatic lesion from my melanoma, but turned out to be a benign lesion. Then, another horseback riding accident where I sustained a concussion, multiple rib fractures and fracture-dislocation of a thumb. Then, I had a boating accident requiring major ankle surgery.

I played hard and worked hard – 100 percent - full throttle all my life, and God has been gracious and good to me to have allowed me the blessings of a long life, in spite of multiple attempts on my part to shorten my life.

I frequently reflect on my father's last moments of his life on earth. Like many of you, I've read numerous accounts of people experiencing near death or after-death experiences, and seeing deceased loved ones in heaven. Two particularly engaging books entitled "90 Minutes in Heaven" and "Heaven is Real." by Don Piper are especially intriguing.

163

But as Dad lay in a hospital bed at Covenant Health System in Lubbock at age 92, where he had received outstanding care, and with his remaining life on earth obviously only minutes away, he, however, remained totally and clearly lucid and coherent.

He had always been in excellent health most of his life, but had had one close brush with death 2 years prior at the age of 90. It was Christmas day and he was at our home with family and friends enjoying a late Christmas lunch. He was seated next to me and carrying on his normal conversation with everyone, when suddenly, without any warning, he collapsed and became unconscious. I caught his upper torso and laid him on the floor next to the dining table. He was not breathing and had no palpable pulse — a sudden cardiac arrest!

Fleetingly, the thought raced through my mind as to what I should do. I asked myself, "Is this God's way of taking my Dad to Heaven — after 90 years of a good life — on Christmas day with family and friends — no pain or suffering?" The last thing he or anyone would want would be for him to be resuscitated and end up with a massive stroke or become a neurologic cripple. Very abruptly, as I was pondering these thoughts, Dr. Sam King, a prominent cardiologist in Lubbock who had been enjoying Christmas in our home for many years with his wife, Carol and daughter, Courtney, and who had also examined Dad as he lay on the floor, said to me, "Bob, Bob, what do you want to do?"

Instinctively, as a physician, your first impulse is to try and save life. And particularly in this instance — here was my own father, a person who only a couple of minutes ago was alive, coherent and talking as intelligently as any of the rest of us at the table. So I immediately replied back to Dr. King, "Well, let's see if we can revive him. You start chest compression, Sam, and I'll give mouth to mouth respirations." I asked my wife, Kay, to call 911 as we started CPR. Within a minute or so his cardiac function returned and he began to regain consciousness. The ambulance arrived soon afterwards and took him on to Methodist Hospital. I had called the ER and asked to speak to the cardiologist on call and it happened to be my good friend, Dr. Gerry Maddoux. Dr. Maddoux rapidly determined that he had not sustained a myocardial infarction as such, but had a cardiac rhythm disturbance resulting in his sudden cardiac arrest (SCA).

Dr. Maddoux subsequently placed a pacemaker in him and he

had a completely uncomplicated hospital stay of a few days, sustaining no neurological impairment whatsoever. When he left the hospital, he said, "Well, I haven't felt this good in years — just a little soreness in my chest" (from Dr. King's cardiac massage).

Dad had another productive two years of life with good quality until a few weeks prior to this current hospitalization when his heart began to fail rather rapidly which led to his present terminal status.

Suddenly with his eyes wide open he said, "I'm crossing the line." My wife, Kay, asked him, "What do you mean, Joe T.?" and he said, "I'm crossing the line into Heaven." We asked him if he saw our Mom - his "Beppy"- and he gave no response, but he had this distinct and steady gaze upon his face and eyes, and everyone in the room knew he was staring at something or someone. He was so intent he couldn't speak. He didn't say, "I see Beppy" or "Heaven is beautiful" but continued to stare for a few more seconds and then closed his eyes, and his soul and spirit moved on to the peace and beauty I know he was experiencing.

I feel reasonably confident he will not be experiencing any more sandstorms or tumbleweeds.

Allan and
Chris Dobbie
in London

Liz and
Allan Dobbie
in London

Chris Dobbie
(center) and
Comrades
in Iraq

Bibliography

- Journal of the Air Force Association, Why Airmen Don't Command, March 2008, p46-7

- Latham Aaron, The Ballard of Gussie and Clyde, Chapter 40, The SWAT Team, Random House, 1997

- Dingus, Georgia Wilson, The Best of Life, The Naylor Co., 1967

- Piper, Don, Heaven is Real, The Berkeley Publishing Group. 2007

- Piper, Don. 90 Minutes in Heaven, Baker Publishing Company, 2004

- Time Life Books, World War II, Battle of the Bulge. 1981

- Sports Illustrated, Scorecard – "Doc" Blanchard, April 27, 2009

- Houston Chronicle Newspaper. May 3rd, 2008

- New York Times Newspaper, In Moscow in 1996, A Doctor's Visit Changed History, May 1, 2007

- Crane, S.L.G, University of Connecticut Libraries, Connecticut History on Line "Le Grippe" June 13, 1908

- St. John, Bob, Heart of a Lion, Taylor Publishing Company, 1991

- Foundation for Advances in Science and Medicine, Profiles in Cardiology, 2003

- Salem, Robert J. Personal Memorabilia

- McCartor, Robert L, Ph.D., Tyner, George S., M.D. Eye of the Storm, Texas Tech Press, 1986

- Roberts, Wendy, Return, Action Printing, 2007